Study Guide and Workbook

CHRIS VON DER HAAR
MARK L. BERENSON
DAVID M. LEVINE
MABEL YU

Department of Statistics and Computer Information Systems
Baruch College, City University of New York

Basic Business Statistics

FOURTH EDITION

CONCEPTS AND APPLICATIONS

MARK L. BERENSON
DAVID M. LEVINE

PRENTICE HALL, ENGLEWOOD CLIFFS, NEW JERSEY 07632

Editorial/production supervision: Brendan M. Stewart
Manufacturing buyer: Laura Crossland

Printed in the United States of America

10 9 8 7 6 5 4 3 2 1

ISBN 0-13-058397-9

Prentice-Hall International (UK) Limited, *London*
Prentice-Hall of Australia Pty. Limited, *Sydney*
Prentice-Hall Canada Inc., *Toronto*
Prentice-Hall Hispanoamericana, S.A, *Mexico*
Prentice-Hall of India Private Limited, *New Delhi*
Prentice-Hall of Japan, Inc., *Tokyo*
Simon & Schuster Asia Pte. Ltd., *Singapore*
Editora Prentice-Hall do Brasil, Ltda., *Rio de Janeiro*

Contents

Preface

The most productive way to learn applied statistical methods is to work out various types of problems as a means of understanding the concepts and methodology involved. The major function of this *Study Guide* is to provide such examples.

We have written the *Study Guide* as a supplement to *Basic Business Statistics: Concepts and Applications*. Each chapter contains several parts. First, the basic concepts covered in the chapter are summarized. This is followed by multiple choice questions (the answers to which are provided in the back of the guide). Next, several examples using the techniques and concepts of the chapter are presented along with their solutions. Finally, review problems for the chapter are given for the student to solve, followed by their solutions.

The *Study Guide* also contains a review of arithmetic and algebra that will be particularly useful to those students with limited exposure to mathematics courses since high school. A diagnostic quiz is provided along with the solutions so the student is made aware of any deficiencies. This appendix will enable the student to focus on the concepts of statistics rather than the mechanics of obtaining solutions.

The authors wish to express their thanks to Susan Davison of Davison Professional Typing Service for typing the *Study Guide* as well as for her editorial assistance.

Chris Von Der Haar
Mark Berenson
David Levine
Mabel Yu

1

Introduction

The subject of statistics encompasses all fields of application from Anthropology to Zoology. Statistical information of all types in all fields is being continually collected, processed, analyzed, and utilized for the purpose of making rational decisions. Chapter 1 focuses on the growth of the subject of statistics and presents several illustrations indicating statistical applications. Such concepts as population versus sample, parameter versus statistic, and statistical description versus statistical inference are considered.

MULTIPLE CHOICE

Match the terms below with their correct definitions.

        a. Population
        b. Statistic
        c. Inferential Statistics
        d. Descriptive Statistics
        e. Parameter
        f. Sample

1. _____   Those methods that make possible the estimation of a characteristic of a population or the making of a decision concerning a population based only on sample results.

2. _____   The totality of items or things under consideration.

3. _____   Those methods involving the collection, presentation, and characterization of a set of data in order to properly describe the various features of that set of data.

4. _____   A summary measure that is computed to describe a characteristic of an entire population.

5. _____   The portion of the population that is selected for analysis.

6. _____   A summary measure that is computed to describe a characteristic from only a sample of the population.

Use the terms given above (a–f) to complete the sentences below.

The Human Resources Department of a large commercial bank wants to study the effect of different management styles on the productivity of its employees. While it would be possible to study all the employees (N=40,000), it would not be practical, so the Human Resources Department selected 500 employees to participate in their study.

7. All the employees in the bank constitute the _____.

8. The 500 employees who will participate in this study constitute the
_____.

The Human Resources Department will draw conclusions about the
(9.) _____ on the basis of information gathered from the
(10.) _____.

A farmer wants to determine the average number of apples per acre in his orchard. In order to do this he randomly selects a number of one-acre plots and counts the number of apples picked from trees on each acre.

11. The average number of apples per acre in his sample is called a _____.

12. The average number of apples per acre computed for all the acres in his orchard is called a _____.

SHORT ANSWER

I.   Suppose you are responsible for developing an advertising campaign to promote an imported beer in America. You decide to conduct a survey to determine attitudes toward imported beer.

Will you survey all Americans? Why or why not?

_____
_____
_____

II. What would you say to your client if he or she asked you about the method of using a sample to draw conclusions about the population?

_____
_____
_____

SOLUTIONS

I.   No. Not only does the cost and time of such a test weigh against surveying a population, but the collection, preparation, and analysis of the data would be unwieldy.

II.   This method is quite reliable since it is based on probability theory and provides researchers with the likelihood that sample results reflect results that would be obtained if the entire population were surveyed.

2

Data Collection

Proper data collection is a most important phase of any research endeavor. Therefore, this chapter examines different types of data, considers different sources of data and, in particular, focuses on the art of questionnaire development and various sampling methods. In addition, problems with respect to coding, editing, and data entry are discussed.

MULTIPLE CHOICE

1. If you record the winning times at a swimming meet as: 34.6 seconds, 35.2 seconds, 37.6 seconds, and 38.2 seconds, can you convert these times to an ordinal level of measurement?

    a. yes
    b. no

2. Can the variable, gender (male or female) be converted to a stronger level of measurement?

    a. yes
    b. no

Use the following information to answer questions 3, 4, and 5.

The Census Bureau gathered the following information about a family in a survey conducted on October 1, 1986.

There were three children in the family. The names and ages of the children were:

Donna	12 years	6 months
David	10 years	2 months
Michael	8 years	10 months

Indicate for questions 3, 4, and 5 whether the variable is:

    a. qualitative
    b. discrete quantitative
    c. continuous quantitative

3. Number of children in this household. _____

4. Names of children in this household. _____

5. Present ages of children in this household. _____

6. Numerical responses which arise from a(n) _____ are called discrete quantitative variables.

    a. counting process
    b. measuring process
    c. open-ended question
    d. closed-ended question

7. Numerical responses which arise from a(n) _____ are called continuous quantitative variables.

    a. counting process
    b. measuring process
    c. open-ended question
    d. closed-ended question

8. Which of the following is true about response rates?

    a. The longer the questionnaire, the lower the response rate.
    b. Mail surveys usually produce lower response rates than personal or telephone surveys.
    c. Question wording can affect a response rate.
    d. All of the above.

9. Pilot testing is an essential phase in conducting a survey because it

    a. provides an estimate of the time needed to complete the survey.
    b. reduces ambiguities in question wording.
    c. may indicate the need for additional questions.
    d. All of the above.

10. If the sample size required for a study is 250 out of a population of 10,000 and you only expect 60% of the chosen subjects to respond favorably, then you should prepare to survey

    a. 150
    b. 250
    c. 417
    d. 500

11. Which of the following types of samples can you use if you want to make statistical inferences from a sample to a population?

    a. cluster sample
    b. judgment sample
    c. simple random sample
    d. both a and c

12. _____ are not selected randomly, so there is no way to know how well they represent the overall population.

   a. Judgment samples
   b. Quota samples
   c. Chunk samples
   d. All of the above

Use the following information to answer questions 13, 14, and 15.

Suppose you are asked to conduct a survey of the members of the American Marketing Association. You are told to use simple random sampling, and you are given a population frame containing N=5,600 names. You decide to use a table of random numbers to select your sample.

13. Since you will sample from a human population, will you sample with or without replacement?

   a. with replacement
   b. without replacement

14. How many digits will the code numbers for each member of your population contain?

   a. one
   b. two
   c. three
   d. four

15. Which of the following code numbers will *not* appear in your list?

   a. 0001
   b. 0250
   c. 3960
   d. 5700

EXAMPLES

I. Indicate the type of data and the level of measurement for each variable below:

   a. Types of automobiles. _____
   b. Annual income. _____
   c. Winners in a marathon by place (1st, 2nd, 3rd, etc.). _____
   d. Winning times of the first 10 runners across a finish line.
      _____
   e. Diameters of bicycle tires. _____
   f. Cooking oil labeled as light, medium, and heavy. _____
   g. Rating of an employee's performance on a 10 point scale.
      _____
   h. Shampoo labeled as dry, normal, oily, and damaged hair.
      _____
   i. Age given as young, middle-aged, and old. _____
   j. Temperature in degrees Fahrenheit. _____

SOLUTION

   a. Qualitative, nominal.
   b. Quantitative, ratio.
   c. Qualitative, ordinal.
   d. Quantitative, ratio.
   e. Quantitative, ratio.
   f. Qualitative, ordinal.
   g. Quantitative, interval.
   h. Qualitative, nominal.
   i. Qualitative, ordinal.
   j. Quantitative, interval.

II. List the three main reasons that explain why statisticians prefer to use sampling procedures instead of taking a complete census.

   _____
   _____
   _____

SOLUTION

Taking a complete census is: (1) too time-consuming, (2) too costly, and (3) too inefficient and cumbersome.

SUPPLEMENT

SUMMATION NOTATION

The symbol "Σ" means the "summation of." Thus:

$$\sum_{i=1}^{n} X_i = X_1 + X_2 + X_3 + \ldots + X_n$$

$$\sum_{i=1}^{n} X_i^2 = X_1^2 + X_2^2 + \ldots + X_n^2$$

and

$$\sum_{i=1}^{n} X_i Y_i = X_1 Y_1 + X_2 Y_2 + \ldots + X_n Y_n$$

Rules of Summation:

Rule 1. $\displaystyle\sum_{i=1}^{n} (X_i + Y_i) = \sum_{i=1}^{n} X_i + \sum_{i=1}^{n} Y_i$

Rule 2. $\displaystyle\sum_{i=1}^{n} (X_i - Y_i) = \sum_{i=1}^{n} X_i - \sum_{i=1}^{n} Y_i$

Rule 3. $\displaystyle\sum_{i=1}^{n} CX_i = C\sum_{i=1}^{n} X_i$

Rule 4. $\displaystyle\sum_{i=1}^{n} C = nC$

The application of the four summation rules provides us with a means of simplifying complex algebraic expressions so that ultimately numerical computations are facilitated.

EXAMPLE

Simplify algebraically and solve numerically the following expression:

$$\sum_{i=1}^{n} (4X_i - Y_i^2 + C)$$

where

$$\sum_{i=1}^{n} X_i = 300 \qquad \sum_{i=1}^{n} Y_i^2 = 169 \qquad C = 100 \qquad n = 5$$

SOLUTION

Using Summation Rules 1 and 2 we have

$$\sum_{i=1}^{n} (4X_i - Y_i^2 + C) = \sum_{i=1}^{n} 4X_i - \sum_{i=1}^{n} Y_i^2 + \sum_{i=1}^{n} C$$

Using Summation Rule 3 we have

$$\sum_{i=1}^{n}4X_i - \sum_{i=1}^{n}Y_i^2 + \sum_{i=1}^{n}C = 4\sum_{i=1}^{n}X_i - \sum_{i=1}^{n}Y_i^2 + \sum_{i=1}^{n}C$$

Using Summation Rule 4 we have

$$4\sum_{i=1}^{n}X_i - \sum_{i=1}^{n}Y_i^2 + \sum_{i=1}^{n}C = 4\sum_{i=1}^{n}X_i - \sum_{i=1}^{n}Y_i^2 + nC$$

and the latter expression is the algebraic simplification. Now to solve numerically, we merely substitute the given information and the following result is obtained:

$$\sum_{i=1}^{n}(4X_i - Y_i^2 + C) = 4\sum_{i=1}^{n}X_i - \sum_{i=1}^{n}Y_i^2 + nC$$

$$= (4)(300) - (169) + (5)(100) = 1,531$$

REVIEW PROBLEM

Simplify algebraically and solve numerically the following expression:

$$\sum_{i=1}^{n}(9X_i^2 + CY_i + 3X_iY_i - 100)$$

where

$$X_1 = 5 \qquad X_2 = 3 \qquad X_3 = 4 \qquad n = 3$$

$$Y_1 = 7 \qquad Y_2 = 2 \qquad Y_3 = 6 \qquad C = 2$$

SOLUTION TO REVIEW PROBLEM

$$\sum_{i=1}^{n}(9X_i^2 + CY_i + 3X_iY_i - 100)$$

$$= \sum_{i=1}^{n}9X_i^2 + \sum_{i=1}^{n}CY_i + \sum_{i=1}^{n}3X_iY_i - \sum_{i=1}^{n}100 \qquad \text{(Rules 1 and 2)}$$

$$= 9\sum_{i=1}^{n}X_i^2 + C\sum_{i=1}^{n}Y_i + 3\sum_{i=1}^{n}X_iY_i - \sum_{i=1}^{n}100 \qquad \text{(Rule 3)}$$

$$= 9\sum_{i=1}^{n}X_i^2 + C\sum_{i=1}^{n}Y_i + 3\sum_{i=1}^{n}X_iY_i - 100n \qquad \text{(Rule 4)}$$

The latter expression is the algebraic simplification. The numerical result is obtained by substitution as follows:

$$\sum_{i=1}^{n} X_i^2 = (5)\,(5) + (3)\,(3) + (4)\,(4) = 50$$

$$\sum_{i=1}^{n} Y_i = 7 + 2 + 6 = 15$$

$$\sum_{i=1}^{n} X_i Y_i = (5)\,(7) + (3)\,(2) + (4)\,(6) = 65$$

Thus,

$$9\sum_{i=1}^{n} X_i^2 + C\sum_{i=1}^{n} Y_i + 3\sum_{i=1}^{n} X_i Y_i - 100n$$

$$= (9)\,(50) + (2)\,(15) + (3)\,(65) - (100)\,(3) = 375$$

3

Describing and Summarizing Data

Once quantitative data have been collected, proper analysis and interpretation are essential. Data have three major properties or characteristics—central tendency, dispersion, and shape. A variety of descriptive summary measures representing these properties may be used to extract and summarize the salient features of the data set. This chapter focuses on the conceptual development, computation, and use of such descriptive measures for data collected in their raw form (ungrouped data).

MULTIPLE CHOICE

1. If all the values in a set of data are the same, the range, the variance, and the standard deviation will be

    a. different.
    b. zero.
    c. one.
    d. cannot be determined without actual data.

2. The greater the spread of scores around the mean,

    a. the larger the range.
    b. the larger the variance.
    c. the larger the standard deviation.
    d. All of the above.

3. The smaller the spread of scores around the mean,

    a. the smaller the range.
    b. the smaller the variance.
    c. the smaller the standard deviation.
    d. All of the above.

4. Which measure of central tendency is based on all the observations in a batch of data?

    a. mean
    b. median
    c. midrange
    d. mode

5. Which of the following measure(s) of central tendency is (are) affected by outliers?

    a. mean
    b. median
    c. midrange
    d. a and c

6. Which of the following is *not* possible?

    a. a negative standard deviation
    b. a positive variance
    c. a standard deviation equal to zero
    d. a variance equal to zero

EXAMPLE

(Ungrouped Data Calculations)

I. A random sample of 15 insurance claims is taken from the August records. The results are as follows:

$	216	254	247	257	231
	265	221	226	228	252
	235	265	272	285	266

A. Compute:

(1) the mean
(2) the median, Q_1, and Q_3
(3) the midhinge
(4) the mode
(5) the range
(6) the interquartile range
(7) the midrange
(8) the variance (definitional and computational)
(9) the standard deviation
(10) the coefficient of variation
(11) the direction of skewness

B. List the five-number summary.

C. Form the box-and-whisker plot.

D. (1) Using the Bienaymé-Chebyshev rule, between what two values would we estimate that at least 75% of the insurance claims are contained?

(2) What percentage of the insurance claims are actually contained within ± 2 standard deviations of the mean?

E. If there are 1,000 insurance claims for August, estimate the total value of these claims.

SOLUTION

A. (1) Computation of the Mean ($\overline{X}$)

(2) Computation of the Median, Q_1 and Q_3

$$\underline{X}$$

$ 216
265
235
254
221
265
247
226
272
257
228
285
231
252
$\underline{266}$

$$\sum_{i=1}^{15} X_i = \$3,720$$

$$\overline{X} = \frac{\sum_{i=1}^{n} X_i}{n} = \frac{3720}{15} = \$248$$

$$\underline{\text{Ordered Array}}$$

$ 216
221
226
228 = Q_1
231
235
247
252 = Median
254
257
265
265 = Q_3
266
272
$\underline{285}$

Positioning Point Locations:

$$\text{Median} = \frac{n+1}{2} = \frac{15+1}{2} = X_{(8)}$$

$$Q_1 = \frac{n+1}{4} = \frac{15+1}{4} = X_{(4)}$$

$$Q_3 = \frac{3(n+1)}{4} = \frac{3(15+1)}{4} = X_{(12)}$$

(3) Midhinge = average of the first and third quartiles = $\dfrac{Q_1 + Q_3}{2}$

$$= \dfrac{(228 + 265)}{2} = \$246.50$$

(4) Mode   = the value that occurs most frequently.

= $265

(5) Range   = largest value minus smallest value = $X_{(n)} - X_{(1)}$

= 285 − 216

= $69

(6) Interquartile range = spread of middle 50% of data

$$= Q_3 - Q_1$$

$$= 265 - 228$$

$$= \$37$$

(7) Midrange = average of smallest and largest values = $\dfrac{X_{(1)} + X_{(n)}}{2}$

$$= \dfrac{216 + 285}{2} = \$250.50$$

(8) Variance = "sort of" the average squared deviation around the mean

Definitional formula for variance: $S^2 = \dfrac{\sum\limits_{i=1}^{n}(X_i - \bar{X})^2}{n - 1}$

X_i	$X_i - \bar{X}$	$(X_i - \bar{X})^2$
216	$216 - 248 = -32$	$(-32)^2 = 1024$
265	$265 - 248 = 17$	$(17)^2 = 289$
235	$235 - 248 = -13$	$(-13)^2 = 169$
254	$254 - 248 = 6$	$(6)^2 = 36$
221	$221 - 248 = -27$	$(-27)^2 = 729$
265	$265 - 248 = 17$	$(17)^2 = 289$
247	$247 - 248 = -1$	$(-1)^2 = 1$
226	$226 - 248 = -22$	$(-22)^2 = 484$
272	$272 - 248 = 24$	$(24)^2 = 576$
257	$257 - 248 = 9$	$(9)^2 = 81$
228	$228 - 248 = -20$	$(-20)^2 = 400$
285	$285 - 248 = 37$	$(37)^2 = 1369$
231	$231 - 248 = -17$	$(-17)^2 = 289$
252	$252 - 248 = 4$	$(4)^2 = 16$
266	$266 - 248 = 18$	$(18)^2 = 324$

$$\sum_{i=1}^{15} X_i = \$3,720 \qquad \sum_{i=1}^{15} (X_i - \bar{X}) = 0 \qquad \sum_{i=1}^{15} (X_i - \bar{X})^2 = 6,076$$

$$\bar{X} = \$248$$

$$S^2 = \frac{6,076}{15 - 1} = 434 \text{ squared dollars}$$

Computational formula for variance:

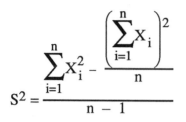

$$S^2 = \frac{\sum\limits_{i=1}^{n} X_i^2 - \dfrac{\left(\sum\limits_{i=1}^{n} X_i\right)^2}{n}}{n-1}$$

X_i	X_i^2
216	$(216)^2 =$ 46,656
265	$(265)^2 =$ 70,225
235	$(235)^2 =$ 55,225
254	$(254)^2 =$ 64,516
221	$(221)^2 =$ 48,841
265	$(265)^2 =$ 70,225
247	$(247)^2 =$ 61,009
226	$(226)^2 =$ 51,076
272	$(272)^2 =$ 73,984
257	$(257)^2 =$ 66,049
228	$(228)^2 =$ 51,984
285	$(285)^2 =$ 81,225
231	$(231)^2 =$ 53,361
252	$(252)^2 =$ 63,504
266	$(266)^2 =$ 70,756
$\sum\limits_{i=1}^{15} X_i = \$3,720$	$\sum\limits_{i=1}^{15} X_i^2 = 928,636$

$$S^2 = \frac{928,636 - \frac{(3,720)^2}{15}}{14} = \frac{928,636 - \frac{13,838,400}{15}}{14}$$

$$S^2 = \frac{928,636 - 922,560}{14} = \frac{6,076}{14}$$

$$S^2 = 434 \text{ squared dollars}$$

(9) Standard deviation =   square root of the average squared deviation around the mean (i.e., the square root of the variance).

$$S = \sqrt{S^2} = \sqrt{434} = \$20.83$$

(10) Coefficient of variation =   measures dispersion relative to the mean.

$$CV = \frac{S}{\overline{X}} \times 100\% = \frac{20.83}{248} = 8.4\%$$

(11) Since $\overline{X} = \$248 <$ Median $= \$252$, the data appear to be somewhat negatively skewed.

B. A five-number summary consists of $X_{(1)}$, Q_1, Median, Q_3, and $X_{(n)}$. For our example, the five number summary is

$X_{(1)}$ = \$216

Q_1 = \$228

Median   = \$252

Q_3 = \$265

$X_{(n)}$ = \$285

C. The Box-and-Whisker plot provides a graphical representation of the data based on the five-number summary.

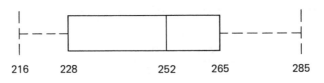

Box-and-Whisker Plot of Insurance Claims

D. (1) From the Bienaymé-Chebyshev rule, at least $(1 - 1/2^2)$ x 100% = 75.0% of the observations must be contained within $\pm$ 2 standard deviations of the mean (i.e., if $1 - 1/k^2 = .75$,

$$\text{then k} = \sqrt{\frac{1}{1 - .75}} = \sqrt{\frac{1}{.25}}$$

$$= \sqrt{4} = 2).$$

Therefore, at least 75.0% of the insurance claims will be between $\overline{X} - 2S$ and $\overline{X} + 2S$ or $\$248 - 2\ (20.83) = \$206.34$ and $\$248 + 2\ (20.83) = \$289.66.$

(2) For these data, the 15 insurance claims fall within $\pm$ 2 standard deviations of the mean. Therefore, 100% of the insurance claims in this sample are between $\$206.34$ and $\$289.66.$

E. Total value = Population size times the sample mean

$$= N\overline{X}$$

Total value = 1,000 ($\$248$) = $\$248,000$

REVIEW PROBLEMS

I. Japanese automobile manufacturers want to show prospective business customers that their companies' compact cars get better gas mileage than the compact cars of the leading American manufacturers. They take a random sample of 8 Japanese cars and 8 American cars. The gas mileages for expressway driving are as follows:

Japanese Cars	American Cars
31	27
39	35
36	35
36	30
33	35
35	36
43	32
27	32

A. For each sample, compute:

(1) the mean

(2) the median

(3) the range

(4) the variance and standard deviation (use computational method)

(5) the coefficient of variation

B. If the Acme company owns 100 Japanese cars and the Bolt company owns 100 American cars, estimate the total traveling miles that each company can hope to get with 100 gallons of gasoline.

C. Write a brief summary report comparing the gas mileage of Japanese cars to American cars.

SOLUTION

A.

	Japanese Cars	American Cars
Ordered Arrays	27 36 31 36 33 39 35 43	27 35 30 35 32 35 32 36
Sample Size	$n = 8$	$n = 8$

	Japanese Cars	American Cars
(1) Mean $$\bar{X} = \frac{\sum\limits_{i=1}^{n} X_i}{n}$$	$$\sum_{i=1}^{8} X_i = 27+31+33+...+43$$ $$= 280$$ $$\bar{X} = \frac{280}{8} = 35.00 \text{ mpg}$$	$$\sum_{i=1}^{8} X_i = 27+30+32+...+36$$ $$= 262$$ $$\bar{X} = \frac{262}{8} = 32.75 \text{ mpg}$$
(2) Median $$\text{Median} = \frac{n+1}{2}$$ ordered value	$\frac{8+1}{2} = 4.5$ ordered value Average 4th and 5th ordered observations $\frac{35+36}{2} = 35.5$ Median = 35.5	$\frac{8+1}{2} = 4.5$ ordered value Average 4th and 5th ordered observations $\frac{32+35}{2} = 33.5$ Median = 33.5
(3) Range $\text{Range} = X_{(n)} - X_{(1)}$	Range = 43 − 27 = 16	Range = 36 − 27 = 9

	Japanese Cars	American Cars
(4) Variance Computational Formula: $S^2 =$ $$\frac{\sum\limits_{i=1}^{n} X_i^2 - \dfrac{\sum\limits_{i=1}^{n}(X_i)^2}{n}}{n-1}$$	$\sum\limits_{1=i}^{8} X_i^2 = 27^2+31^2+33^2+...+43^2$ $= 9{,}966$ $\sum\limits_{i=1}^{8} X_i = 280$ $S^2 = \dfrac{9{,}966 - \dfrac{(280)^2}{8}}{7}$ $= \dfrac{166}{7} = 23.71$	$\sum\limits_{1=i}^{8} X_i^2 = 27^2+30^2+32^2+...+36^2$ $= 8{,}648$ $\sum\limits_{i=1}^{8} X_i = 262$ $S^2 = \dfrac{8{,}648 - \dfrac{(262)^2}{8}}{7}$ $= \dfrac{67.5}{7} = 9.64$
Standard Deviation $S = \sqrt{S^2}$	$S = \sqrt{23.71} = 4.87$	$S = \sqrt{9.64} = 3.10$
(5) Coefficient of Variation $CV = \dfrac{S}{\overline{X}} \times 100\%$	$CV = \dfrac{4.87}{35} \times 100\%$ $= 13.91\%$	$CV = \dfrac{3.10}{32.75} \times 100\%$ $= 9.47\%$

B.

	Japanese Cars	American Cars
Mean Standard deviation Population size	$\overline{X}$ = 35.00 mpg S = 4.87 mpg N = 100 Acme	$\overline{X}$ = 32.75 mpg S = 3.10 mpg N = 100 Bolt
Total Total = $N\overline{X}$	Total = (100) (35.00) = 3,500 miles	Total = (100) (32.75) = 3,275 miles

C.   Based on these sample results, Japanese compact cars get better gas mileage than American compact cars. The mean miles per gallon for Japanese cars is 35.00 mpg compared to 32.75 mpg for American cars. The median miles per gallon for Japanese cars (35.5 mpg) is also larger than that for American cars (33.5 mpg).

    A comparison of the standard deviations for the gas mileage of Japanese versus American compact cars shows greater variability for Japanese cars (4.87 mpg) than for American cars (3.10). The coefficient of variation also shows that there is more relative variation in gas mileage for Japanese cars (13.91%) than in gas mileage for American cars (9.47%).

II. A professor taught four sections of an introductory statistics course. The final exam scores for each class are given below.

Class #1	Class #2	Class #3	Class #4
58	61	22	60
59	69	33	65
61	69	46	67
62	70	57	69
70	70	68	70
82	79	86	70
90	82	95	71
91	82	96	73
93	100	97	75
95	100	100	80

A. Using the exam scores for Classes #1 and #2, calculate the median, mean, standard deviation and coefficient of variation to complete the table below.

	Class #1	Class #2	Class #3	Class #4
Median =	_____	_____	77.00	70.00
$\bar{X}$ =	_____	_____	70.00	70.00
S =	_____	_____	29.07	5.48
CV =	_____	_____	41.53%	7.83%

B. (1) If you sum the deviations of each score from the mean for each set of data above, will this always equal zero?

_____

(2) What does this tell you about the mean?

_____

_____

C. Using the data for Class #1, choose any value larger than the mean, subtract it from each score, square the deviations, and then sum the deviations, i.e.,

$$\sum_{i=1}^{n}(X_i - X_L)^2$$

where X_L is any value larger than the mean.

Compare this sum with the sum of the squared deviations of each score from the mean. (1) Which value is larger?

_____

Choose any value smaller than the mean and repeat the same procedure. Compare this sum with the sum of the squared deviations of each score from the mean. (2) Which value is larger?

_____

(3) What do these comparisons tell you about the mean?

_____

_____

D. Study the data for Class #2. (1) Which scores in this class have the greatest weight in determining the standard deviation?

_____

(2) What does this indicate about the use of the standard deviation as a measure of dispersion when there are a few extreme cases (i.e., outliers)?

_____

_____

E. Compare the exam scores for Class #1 and Class #2. Notice that the mean for Class #1 is 76.1 and its median is 76; the mean for Class #2 is 78.2 and its median is 74.5. Is a professor justified in concluding that Class #2 did better on this exam than Class #1? Why or why not?

_____

_____

_____

F. Compare the exam scores for Class #3 and Class #4. Notice that the mean for both classes is 70.0 but that each of the other statistics is different. (1) If you were a professor, which of the four classes do you think would be easier to teach? Why?

_____

_____

_____

(2) Which class has the most homogeneous batch of data?

_____

SOLUTION

A.

	Class #1			Class #2	
X_i	$(X_i - \bar{X})$	$(X_i - \bar{X})^2$	X_i	$(X_i - \bar{X})$	$(X_i - \bar{X})^2$
58	−18.1	327.61	61	−17.2	295.84
59	−17.1	292.41	69	−9.2	84.64
61	−15.1	228.01	69	−9.2	84.64
62	−14.1	198.81	70	−8.2	67.24
70	−6.1	37.21	70	−8.2	67.24
82	5.9	34.81	79	.8	.64
90	13.9	193.21	82	3.8	14.44
91	14.9	222.01	82	3.8	14.44
93	16.9	285.61	100	21.8	475.24
95	18.9	357.21	100	21.8	475.24
761.0	0.0	2,176.90	782.0	0.0	1,579.60
$\sum_{i=1}^{10} X_i$	$\sum_{i=1}^{10}(X_i - \bar{X})$	$\sum_{i=1}^{10}(X_i - \bar{X})^2$	$\sum_{i=1}^{10} X_i$	$\sum_{i=1}^{10}(X_i - \bar{X})$	$\sum_{i=1}^{10}(X_i - \bar{X})^2$

Median = 76.00   Median = 74.50

$\bar{X}_1$ = 76.10 $\bar{X}_2$ = 78.20

S_1 = 15.55 S_2 = 13.25

CV = 20.43%   CV = 16.94%

B. (1) Yes.
   (2) The mean acts as a "balancing point" so that observations which are smaller balance out those which are larger.

C. (1) The sum which replaces the mean with a larger value.

(2) The sum which replaces the mean with a smaller value.

(3) Since the mean is a "balancing point," the sum of the squared differences of each observation from the mean is less than the squared differences obtained from any other value.

D. (1) The scores of 100.

(2) Since the squaring process involved in calculating the standard deviation gives more relative weight to extreme cases, this may mislead us. If outliers are so extreme so that the standard deviation is unusually large, we should indicate the effect of these cases and consider an alternative measure of dispersion to describe these data.

E. No. Extreme values (100's) present in Class #2 cause a noticeable effect on the mean. In this case the median should be used to compare class scores. This comparison shows that Class #1 (76.0) did better than Class #2 (74.5).

F. (1) Although the means for these classes are identical, the standard deviations and coefficients of variation indicate substantial differences in the variability of exam scores. Since there is less variability in the scores of Class #4, the students appear to be more similar in their abilities. This should make it easier for a professor to prepare lectures. The greater variability in Class #3 suggests that a professor must try to teach students at several different levels, making it difficult to maintain the interest of all students at once.

(2) As indicated above, Class #4 has the most homogeneous batch of data.

III. The Dean in the Financial Aid Office would like to determine whether the expenses of fine arts students are more variable than those of music students. He finds that the average cost per semester for textbooks, fees, and supplies for students majoring in fine arts is $375 with a standard deviation of $15; the average cost for textbooks, fees, and supplies for music students at the same university is $150 with a standard deviation of $10. What can the Dean conclude on the basis of these results? Compare the variability of the costs of an education for art and music students (a) on an absolute basis and (b) on a relative basis.

_____

_____

SOLUTION

(a) Since the standard deviation for a student's expenses is greater for fine arts students ($15) than for music students ($10), the absolute variability in expenses is greater for fine arts students.

(b) However, relative to the mean value of expenses for each group, there is more variability in expenses for music students (6.6%) than in the expenses for fine arts students (4.0%).

Fine Arts Students	Music Students
$CV = \dfrac{S}{\overline{X}} \times 100\%$	$CV = \dfrac{S}{\overline{X}} \times 100\%$
$= \dfrac{15}{375} \times 100\%$	$= \dfrac{10}{150} \times 100\%$
$= 4.0\%$	$= 6.7\%$

IV. The Vice-President in charge of marketing research for a large commercial bank would like to determine whether the length of research analysts' reports is more variable than the time taken to write the reports. A record of the projects completed during a six month period of time showed that the average time analysts took to complete a report was 87 hours with a standard deviation of 5 hours; the average length of the reports was 35 pages with a standard deviation of 3 pages. What can the Vice-President conclude about the relative variability of these two variables?

SOLUTION

The coefficient of variation for the time taken to complete a report is 5.74% compared to a coefficient of variation of 8.57% for the length of a report. Thus, on a relative basis there is more variability in the length of research reports.

Time to Write Report	Length of Report
$CV_{Time} = \dfrac{5}{87} \times 100\%$	$CV_{Length} = \dfrac{3}{35} \times 100\%$
$= 5.75\%$	$= 8.57\%$

4

Data Presentation

A common problem faced by the researcher is how to properly summarize and present massive amounts of data that are collected in raw form so that the salient features of the data are more easily understood. Qualitative data may be tallied and presented as bar charts, as pie charts, as dot charts, or, where appropriate, as tables of cross-classification. On the other hand, quantitative data are often prepared and organized for tabular and chart presentation by forming ordered arrays and/or stem-and-leaf displays. (See Chapter 3.) However, to present the data in its most usual format, various tables (frequency distributions, percentage or relative frequency distributions, and cumulative distributions) and charts (histograms, polygons and ogives) are constructed. This chapter then focuses on methods of tabular and chart presentation as an aid to data analysis and interpretation.

MULTIPLE CHOICE

1. When polygons or histograms are constructed, which axis must show the true zero or "origin"?

    a. horizontal
    b. vertical
    c. both horizontal and vertical
    d. neither horizontal nor vertical

2. Why is it necessary to connect the first and last midpoints of a polygon with the horizontal axis?

    a. for aesthetic reasons
    b. because the area under the percentage distribution must be 100.0%
    c. to prevent the reader from mistaking this graph for an ogive
    d. a and c

3. For what type of data are bar charts, pie charts, or dot charts appropriate?

    a. qualitative data
    b. discrete quantitative data
    c. continuous quantitative data
    d. b and c

4. _____ allow us to compare two or more batches of data in one picture.

    a. histograms
    b. pie charts
    c. dot charts
    d. polygons

5. How does polygon A differ from polygon B?

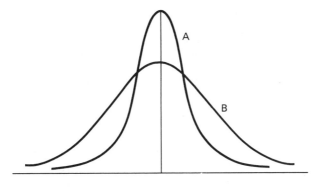

    a. different means
    b. different dispersions
    c. different means and dispersions
    d. different areas under the curve

6. The ogive illustrated here represents the cumulative percentage of students' grades for the first exam. The median is approximately

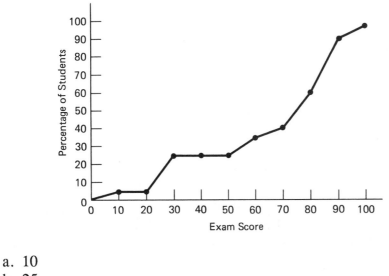

    a. 10
    b. 25
    c. 50
    d. 75

7. A disc jockey conducted a survey of 400 Americans (100 each from the north, east, west, and south) to determine whether people in different parts of the country preferred different types of music. The table below shows the results of this survey.

Music Preference	Parts of Country				
	North	East	West	South	Totals
Classical	5.00%	10.00%	5.00%	5.00%	25.00%
Jazz	6.25%	6.25%	10.00%	6.25%	28.75%
Hard Rock	7.50%	5.00%	5.00%	5.00%	22.50%
Country Western	3.75%	2.50%	2.50%	15.00%	23.75%
Totals	22.50%	23.75%	22.50%	31.25%	100.00%

Are the percentages in this table based on the overall total, row totals, or column totals?

    a. overall total
    b. row totals
    c. column totals
    d. cannot be determined on the basis of the given information

EXAMPLES

I. A paint company sets monthly sales goals for its salespersons and awards bonuses to salespersons who reach their goal nine out of twelve times. The data below show the number of salespersons reaching their goal in January in each of the company's 90 districts (100 salespersons are assigned to each district).

88	63	88	68	75	66	87	79	77
72	74	76	74	66	79	76	67	66
56	79	64	77	80	52	95	84	75
68	54	45	92	87	74	62	79	60
81	67	81	80	74	71	61	93	77
73	83	64	71	84	87	78	61	65
91	75	74	57	69	78	16	72	74
88	70	82	80	73	76	75	51	95
61	68	67	66	87	76	71	70	86
60	80	65	90	76	92	75	88	78

A. (1) Place the raw data in an ordered array;

(2) Place the raw data in a stem-and-leaf display;

(3) Form three frequency distributions with these data:
   (a) for the first, use interval widths of 5.
   (b) for the second, use interval widths of 10.
   (c) for the third, use interval widths of 20.

(4) Compare the frequency distributions you formed to answer the following questions:
   (a) Which of these distributions shows the most even or smooth distribution of data?
   (b) In which frequency distribution do you obscure much of the raw data, i.e., lose much of the original information?
   (c) In which frequency distribution is the picture so detailed that it is difficult to summarize the data?
   (d) Which frequency distribution presents the best picture of the data? Why?

(5) Use the frequency distribution with interval widths of 10 to:
   (a) form the relative frequency and percentage distributions.
   (b) form the cumulative percentage distribution.
   (c) plot the frequency histogram.
   (d) plot the ogive.

(6) Refer to the histogram you formed in (5c) to answer the following questions:
   (a) Are the heights of the bars in this histogram proportional to the frequencies in each interval?
   (b) Are the intervals of equal width?
   (c) For each bar in this histogram indicate the proportion of cases contained in the interval as a fraction, e.g., the first bar will be 0/90.
   (d) If the width of each rectangle in this histogram is one unit and the height is the proportion that you have indicated, what is the total area under the histogram?
   (e) Superimpose a frequency polygon on top of the histogram you drew. Is the area under the frequency polygon equal to the area under the frequency histogram? Explain how the superimposed figure illustrates that the areas must be equal.

SOLUTION

(1) Ordered array of number of salespersons reaching January sales goals.

16	61	66	70	74	76	79	82	88
45	61	66	71	74	76	79	83	88
51	62	67	71	74	76	79	84	88
52	63	67	71	74	76	79	84	90
54	64	67	72	75	77	80	86	91
56	64	68	72	75	77	80	87	92
57	65	68	73	75	77	80	87	92
60	65	68	73	75	78	80	87	93
60	66	69	74	75	78	81	87	95
61	66	70	74	76	78	81	88	95

(2) Stem-and-leaf display.

1	6
2	
3	
4	5
5	12467
6	0011123445566667778889
7	00111223344444455555666667778889999
8	00001123446777788888
9	0122355

(3a) Data classified into intervals of width 5.

Salespersons Reaching January Sales Goals	Frequency Tallies	
0.0 but less than 5.0		0
5.0 but less than 10.0		0
10.0 but less than 15.0		0
15.0 but less than 20.0		1
20.0 but less than 25.0		0
25.0 but less than 30.0		0
30.0 but less than 35.0		0
35.0 but less than 40.0		0
40.0 but less than 45.0		0
45.0 but less than 50.0	/	1
50.0 but less than 55.0	///	3
55.0 but less than 60.0	//	2
60.0 but less than 65.0	₩₩ ////	9
65.0 but less than 70.0	₩₩ ₩₩ ///	13
70.0 but less than 75.0	₩₩ ₩₩ ₩₩	15
75.0 but less than 80.0	₩₩ ₩₩ ₩₩ ₩₩	20
80.0 but less than 85.0	₩₩ ₩₩	10
85.0 but less than 90.0	₩₩ ////	9
90.0 but less than 95.0	₩₩	5
95.0 but less than 100.0	//	2
		90

(3b)   Data classified into intervals of width 10.

Salespersons Reaching January Sales Goals	Frequency Tallies	
0.0 but less than 10.0		0
10.0 but less than 20.0	/	1
20.0 but less than 30.0		0
30.0 but less than 40.0		0
40.0 but less than 50.0	/	1
50.0 but less than 60.0	⟍⟍⟍⟍⟍	5
60.0 but less than 70.0	⟍⟍⟍⟍ ⟍⟍⟍⟍ ⟍⟍⟍⟍ ⟍⟍⟍⟍ //	22
70.0 but less than 80.0	⟍⟍⟍⟍ ⟍⟍⟍⟍ ⟍⟍⟍⟍ ⟍⟍⟍⟍ ⟍⟍⟍⟍ ⟍⟍⟍⟍ ⟍⟍⟍⟍	35
80.0 but less than 90.0	⟍⟍⟍⟍ ⟍⟍⟍⟍ ⟍⟍⟍⟍ ////	19
90.0 but less than 100.0	⟍⟍⟍⟍ //	7
		$\overline{90}$

(3c)   Data classified into intervals of width 20.

Salespersons Reaching January Sales Goals	Frequency Tallies	
0.0 but less than 20.0	/	1
20.0 but less than 40.0		0
40.0 but less than 60.0	⟍⟍⟍⟍ /	6
60.0 but less than 80.0	⟍⟍⟍⟍ ⟍⟍⟍⟍ ⟍⟍⟍⟍ ⟍⟍⟍⟍ ⟍⟍⟍⟍ ⟍⟍⟍⟍ ⟍⟍⟍⟍ ⟍⟍⟍⟍ ⟍⟍⟍⟍ ⟍⟍⟍⟍ ⟍⟍⟍⟍ //	57
80.0 but less than 100.0	⟍⟍⟍⟍ ⟍⟍⟍⟍ ⟍⟍⟍⟍ ⟍⟍⟍⟍ ⟍⟍⟍⟍ /	26
		$\overline{90}$

(4)

    (a) The frequency distribution with data classified into intervals of width 10.

    (b) The frequency distribution with data classified into intervals of width 20.

    (c) The frequency distribution with data classified into intervals of width 5.

    (d) The frequency distribution with data classified into intervals of width 10 because the data appear to be the most evenly distributed. The picture is not so detailed as to be confusing nor too condensed as to obscure information.

(5a)   Relative and Percentage Distributions.

Salespersons Reaching January Sales Goals	Relative Frequency	Percentage
0.0 but less than 10.0	0.000	0.0
10.0 but less than 20.0	0.011	1.1
20.0 but less than 30.0	0.000	0.0
30.0 but less than 40.0	0.000	0.0
40.0 but less than 50.0	0.011	1.1
50.0 but less than 60.0	0.056	5.6
60.0 but less than 70.0	0.244	24.4
70.0 but less than 80.0	0.389	38.9
80.0 but less than 90.0	0.211	21.1
90.0 but less than 100.0	0.078	7.8
	1.000	100.0%

(5b)   Cumulative Percentage Distribution.

Salespersons Reaching
January Sales Goals

Number of Cases "Less Than" Lower Boundary of Class Interval	Cumulative Frequency	Cumulative Percentage
0.0	0	0.0
10.0	0	0.0
20.0	1	1.1
30.0	1	1.1
40.0	1	1.1
50.0	2	2.2
60.0	7	7.8
70.0	29	32.2
80.0	64	71.1
90.0	83	92.2
100.0	90	100.0

(5c)   Frequency Histogram of Salespersons Reaching January Sales Goals in a Company's 90 Districts.

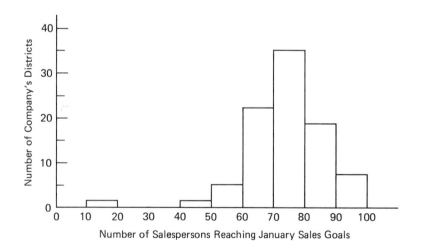

(5d)   Ogive—Cumulative Percentage Polygon of Number of Salespersons Reaching January Sales Goals in a Company's 90 Districts.

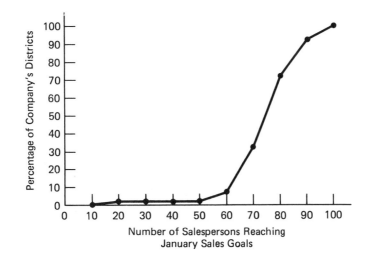

(6)

(a) Yes.

(b) Yes.

(c) 0/90; 1/90; 0/90; 0/90; 1/90; 5/90; 22/90; 35/90; 19/90; 7/90

(d) (1) (0/90) + (1) (1/90) + (1) (0/90) + (1) (0/90) + (1) (1/90) +
    (1) (5/90) + (1) (22/90) + (1) (35/90) + (1) (19/90) + (1) (7/90) =
    90/90 = 1

(e) Yes. Every small triangle which lies inside the frequency polygon but outside of the histogram is matched by a triangle with exactly the same area which lies within the histogram but outside of the frequency polygon.

Frequency Polygon Superimposed on Frequency Histogram (5c)

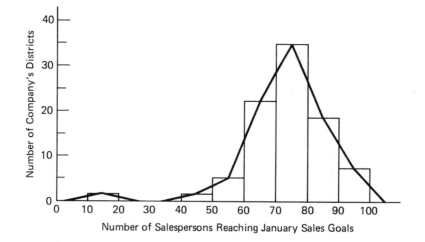

(Grouped Data Approximations)

II. A marketing research firm reports the following distribution of billings to clients from a sample of 100 accounts.

Total Cost of Project	Number of Accounts (f)
$ 0 but less than $ 5,000	9
$ 5,000 but less than $10,000	10
$ 10,000 but less than $15,000	12
$ 15,000 but less than $20,000	15
$ 20,000 but less than $25,000	21
$ 25,000 but less than $30,000	23
$ 30,000 but less than $35,000	10
Total	100

A. Find the arithmetic mean.
B. Find the variance (definitional).
C. Find the standard deviation.

SOLUTION

A.   Computation of the arithmetic mean.

Cost of Project (in thousands)	Class Midpoints m_j	Number of Accounts f_j	m_jf_j
$ 0 but less than $ 5	2.5	9	22.50
$ 5 but less than $ 10	7.5	10	75.00
$ 10 but less than $ 15	12.5	12	150.00
$ 15 but less than $ 20	17.5	15	262.50
$ 20 but less than $ 25	22.5	21	472.50
$ 25 but less than $ 30	27.5	23	632.50
$ 30 but less than $ 35	32.5	10	325.00
Totals		100	$1,940.00

$$\sum_{j=1}^{g} m_jf_j$$

(*Note:* g = number of groups or classes in frequency distribution)

$$\bar{X} \cong \frac{\sum_{j=1}^{g} m_jf_j}{n} = \frac{\$1,940}{100} = \$19.40$$

B. Computation of variance using definitional method.

Definitional formula for variance:

$$S^2 = \frac{\displaystyle\sum_{j=1}^{g} (m_j - \bar{X})^2 \, f_j}{n - 1}$$

Cost of Project (in thousands)	Class Midpoints m_j	$(m_j - \bar{X})$	$(m_j - \bar{X})^2$	Number of Accounts f_j	$(m_j - \bar{X})^2 \, f_j$
$ 0 but less than $ 5	2.5	−16.9	285.61	9	2,570.49
$ 5 but less than $10	7.5	−11.9	141.61	10	1,416.10
$10 but less than $15	12.5	− 6.9	47.61	12	571.32
$15 but less than $20	17.5	− 1.9	3.61	15	54.15
$20 but less than $25	22.5	3.1	9.61	21	201.81
$25 but less than $30	27.5	8.1	65.61	23	1,509.03
$30 but less than $35	32.5	13.1	171.61	10	1,716.10
Totals				100	8,039.00

$\bar{X} = \$19.40$

$$S^2 = \sum_{j=1}^{g} \frac{(m_j - \bar{X})^2 \, f_j}{n - 1} = \frac{8,039.00}{99} = 81.20202$$

(Converted to thousands 81,202.02)

C. Standard deviation $= \sqrt{S^2} = \sqrt{81.20202} = \$9.011$

REVIEW PROBLEMS

I. For the data below indicate how the following changes would affect the mean and median (increase, decrease, no effect).

a. Increase the frequency in the last interval (90-99) to 20.

b. Increase all intervals by 10 (i.e., 40-49, 50-59, 60-69, etc.) but keep the frequencies the same.

c. Keeping the original intervals, take three cases from the 60-69 interval and put them in the 70-79 interval.

d. Triple the frequencies in each of the original intervals.

e. Change the last interval to 90-109.

Data	Frequency	Cumulative Frequency
30-39	9	9
40-49	10	19
50-59	12	31
60-69	15	46
70-79	21	67
80-89	23	90
90-99	10	100
	100	

SOLUTION

a.   mean increases; median increases.
b.   mean increases; median increases.
c.   mean increases; median increases.
d.   mean stays the same; median stays the same.
e.   mean increases; median stays the same.

II. A study was conducted by the Life Insurance Marketing Research Association that compared the attitudes of men and women toward the purchase of life-insurance. A sample of 150 women and 125 men was asked if it was necessary for a wife to purchase $100,000 worth of life-insurance to protect her family in case of her death. The results are shown below.

Response	Women	Men
Yes	75	50
No	75	75

A. Construct a table with column percentages.

B. What would you conclude from this study?

SOLUTION

A.

Response	Women	Men
Yes	50%	40%
No	50%	60%
Totals	100%	100%

B. Women are more likely than men to say that they feel it is necessary for a wife to purchase $100,000 worth of life-insurance to protect her family in case of her death.

III. A study was conducted to investigate the relationship between an individual's financial success and his or her attitudes toward success. A sample of individuals who had low, medium, and high financial success was asked whether success was due primarily to effort or to luck. The results are shown below.

| | -----------Financial Success----------- | | | |
	Low	Medium	High	Totals
Effort	25	100	90	215
Luck	100	50	10	160
Totals	125	150	100	375

a. What is the percentage of individuals in the total sample believing that effort is most important to one's success?

b. What percentage of individuals who believe that effort is most important are high financial success individuals?

c. What is the percentage of high financial success individuals who believe that effort is most important to one's success?

d. Why do your answers to a, b, and c differ?

e. Are there relatively more individuals believing effort is most important among high financial success individuals than among low financial success individuals? Answer in terms of percentages.

SOLUTION

a. 215/375 = 57.3%
b. 90/215 = 41.9%
c. 90/100 = 90.0%
d. The percentages are based on different totals, i.e., row, column, or overall totals.
e. There are relatively more high financial success individuals than low financial success individuals believing that effort is most important for success, i.e., 90/100 = 90% versus 25/125 = 20%.

IV. Due to a substantial decline in the value of its stock, a large commercial bank decided that it must reduce its expenses. A consulting firm has recommended three types of cutbacks: reducing staff, reducing the advertising budget, and reducing the budget for entertaining business clients. A survey was conducted to assess how top management in the bank felt about these recommendations. The sample consisted of 100 decision-makers in retail banking, 100 decision-makers in wholesale banking, and 100 decision-makers in investment banking. The results showed that 15 retail bankers were for reducing staff as were 35 wholesale bankers and 90 investment bankers. Five retail bankers were in favor of reducing the advertising budget as were 55 wholesale bankers and 85 investment bankers. Fifteen retail bankers were for reducing the entertainment budget as were 20 wholesale bankers and 25 investment bankers.

Form a supertable of these responses.

SOLUTION

A SUPERTABLE FOR STUDYING THE RELATIONSHIPS BETWEEN DIFFERENT BANK SECTORS AND REACTIONS TO RECOMMENDED BUDGET CUTS

Variables and Category Percentages	------------------ Bank Sector ------------------		
	Retail Banking	Wholesale Banking	Investment Banking
Reduce Staff			
For (46.7%)	10.7%	25.0%	64.3%
Against (53.3%)	53.1%	40.6%	6.3%
Reduce Advertising Budget			
For (48.3%)	3.4%	37.9%	58.6%
Against (51.7%)	61.3%	29.0%	9.7%
Reduce Entertainment Budget			
For (20.0%)	25.0%	33.3%	41.7%
Against (80.0%)	35.4%	33.3%	31.3%

V. A securities analysis firm requires job applicants to take an exam in order to determine whether they possess the skills needed for the job. This exam is given every spring to business students interested in positions after they graduate. The figure below shows the cumulative relative frequency polygons (ogives) of exam scores for two random samples (A and B) of 100 students each drawn from two business schools in New York City. Based on these data, answer each of the following questions.

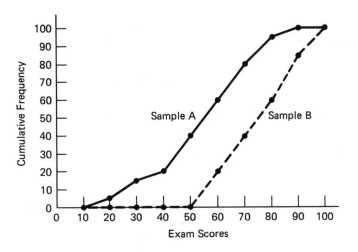

A. For both samples approximate the following:

1. the median.

2. Q_1.

3. Q_3.

4. the midhinge.

5. the interquartile range.

B. On the basis of your answers to A, what can you say about the shape of the data for samples A and B?

C.
1. What percentage of students in sample A received exam scores below 50?

   _____

2. What percentage of students in sample B received exam scores below 50?

   _____

3. What percentage of students in sample A received exam scores of 50 or better? _____

4. What percentage of students in sample B received exam scores of 50 or better? _____

D. On the basis of these results, which sample (A or B) has the better students?

   _____

SOLUTION

A.
1. sample A: $Q_2 = 55$; sample B: $Q_2 = 75$.
2. sample A: $Q_1 = 42$; sample B: $Q_1 = 61$.
3. sample A: $Q_3 = 67$; sample B: $Q_3 = 85$.
4. sample A: 54.5; sample B: 73.
5. sample A: 25; sample B: 24.

B. The data in sample A, which resemble an "S" in this cumulative frequency polygon, are more or less evenly distributed, resembling a bell-shaped curve. The data in sample B, which form a nearly straight line in this cumulative frequency polygon, appear to be slightly right-skewed.

C.
1. 40%
2. 0%
3. 60%
4. 100%

D. Sample B.

VI. A student who was studying for his SATs recorded the number of minutes to solve 20 math problems. His data for 21 consecutive days are presented below:

	Sun.	Mon.	Tue.	Wed.	Thu.	Fri.	Sat.
1st week	92	95	91	87	83	76	80
2nd week	74	75	72	70	70	68	67
3rd week	64	64	62	60	58	55	52

(a) Form a digidot plot for his data.
(b) What can you conclude from this plot?

SOLUTION

(a)

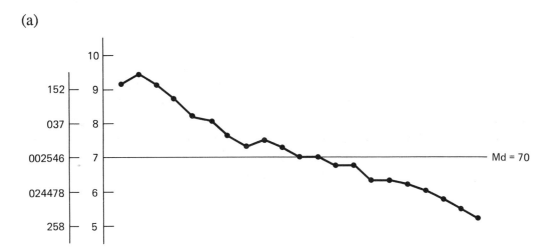

(b) This digidot plot shows a negative trend in the data. As time passes, the positive results of this student's studying are reflected in his ability to solve problems in less time.

5

Using the Computer for Descriptive Statistical Analysis

To this point we have studied how collected data are prepared, summarized, characterized, and presented. This chapter discusses how appropriate computer software can help us in statistically analyzing our data. To interact properly with the computer, the user must be familiar with the software packages currently on the market, as well as know how to select appropriate statistical procedures for the tasks at hand. For further discussion and a more detailed outline of how this may be accomplished, please refer to Chapter 5 in your textbook.

6

Basic Probability

In this chapter various rules of probability are examined. The concept of an event and a sample space are developed to provide a means of evaluating simple and joint probabilities using either a contingency table or Venn diagram. These principles are extended to conditional probability, the multiplication rule, and the addition rule. Conditional probability is illustrated by using Bayes' theorem (for revising probabilities). Various counting rules, including permutations and combinations, are then discussed for situations in which there are a larger number of favorable outcomes.

MULTIPLE CHOICE

1. In a version of a board game, players roll dice and move around a game board. The goal of the game is to accumulate as much property as possible. Whenever a player lands on property, he or she may buy that property if it is not yet owned. There is a total of 28 cards which may be identified by the color of the card, its name, and its cost. The composition of the deck is given below.

Color of Card	Property Name	Property Cost
Dark Purple (2)	Mutnick Avenue	$ 60
	Berenson Avenue	$ 60
Light Blue (3)	October Avenue	$100
	Veronica Avenue	$100
	Conrad Avenue	$120
Purple (3)	Sycamore Place	$140
	Sugar Maple Avenue	$140
	Victoria Avenue	$160
Gold (3)	Sugar Tom's Place	$180
	Touchdown Avenue	$180
	Northville Avenue	$200
Red (3)	Kaintuck Avenue	$220
	Ixtapa Avenue	$220
	Iroquois Avenue	$240
Yellow (3)	Aspen Avenue	$260
	Venus Place	$260
	Mark Gardens	$260
Green (3)	Palisade Avenue	$300
	North Gate Avenue	$300
	Pharaoh Avenue	$320
Dark Blue (2)	Pink Place	$350
	Whitney Circle	$400
Black & White Bus Companies (4)	White Dog	$200
	Safe Trail	$200
	Intercity	$200
	Cross Country	$200
Black & White Utility Companies (2)	Farout Lighting Company	$150
	Running Water Company	$150

Using the information given about the property above, answer the following questions:

1. What approach to the subject of probability does the chance of picking a green card from the deck of cards exemplify?

    a. a priori classical probability
    b. empirical classical probability
    c. subjective probability
    d. a posteriori classical probability

2. The collection of all the property in the deck of 28 cards is called the

    a. simple event
    b. joint event
    c. complement of an event
    d. sample space

3. If you randomly select a card from the deck, what is the probability that it is Kaintuck Avenue?

    a. 1/3
    b. 1/28
    c. 3/28
    d. 1/84

4. If you randomly select a card from the deck, what is the probability that it is a bus company?

    a. 1/7
    b. 4/7
    c. 1/4
    d. 1/256

5. What is the probability that the card is gold and costs $180?

    a. 1/28
    b. 1/14
    c. 1/7
    d. 2/3

6. What is the probability that the card is red or costs $200?

     a. 2/7
     b. 3/7
     c. 15/784
     d. 3/196

7. If we know the card is light blue, what is the probability that it is also October Avenue?

     a. 1/3
     b. 1/28
     c. 3/28
     d. 3/84

8. Let's say we are interested in two variables—"cost of property" and "color of card." The contingency table is shown below.

| Cost of Property | ----------------Color of Card--------------- | | |
	Black and White	Not Black and White	Totals
$200	4	1	5
Not $200	2	21	23
Totals	6	22	28

How many events does each variable have?

     a. one: (A)
     b. two: (A and A', B and B')
     c. three: (A, A', B)
     d. four: (A, A', B, B')

9. Let   A   = $200
       A' = Not $200
       B   = Black and White
       B' = Not Black and White

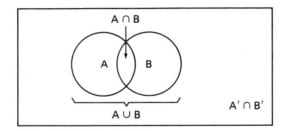

What does A∪B equal?

    a. 4
    b. 7
    c. 21
    d. 28

10. What does A∩B equal?

    a. 4
    b. 7
    c. 21
    d. 28

11. What does A'∩B' equal?

    a. 4
    b. 7
    c. 21
    d. 28

12. Probabilities range in value from

    a. −1 to +1
    b. 0 to +1
    c. 0 to 100
    d. 1 to 100

13. The probability of selecting a property that costs $200 is called a

    a. simple probability
    b. marginal probability
    c. joint probability
    d. a and b

14. The probability of selecting a property that costs $200 and is black and white is called a

    a. simple probability
    b. marginal probability
    c. joint probability
    d. a and b

15. The event "selecting a property that costs $200" from the deck is an example of a

    a. simple event
    b. joint event
    c. sample space
    d. complement of an event

16. The events "black and white" and "not black and white" are

    a. mutually exclusive
    b. collectively exhaustive
    c. joint events
    d. a and b

17. The number of ways that 6 runners can be lined up at the starting line would be computed from

    a. 6^6
    b. (6) (6)
    c. 6!
    d. 6!/(5! 1!)

18. The number of ways that 5 kinds of candies can be selected from 12 kinds of candies for an assorted gift box would be computed from

>   a. 5^{12}
>   b. (5) (12)
>   c. 12!/7!
>   d. 12!/(5! 7!)

EXAMPLE

I. An insurance company is studying the rates of car accidents in three different communities. They randomly selected 1,500 automobile owners in these communities and mailed a questionnaire to each asking whether he or she had been involved in a car accident during the past two years. The table below shows the results of this survey.

Involved in a car accident during last two years	Community A	Community B	Community C	Totals
(Y) Yes	72	93	164	329
(Y') No	378	407	386	1,171
Totals	450	500	550	1,500

A. If an automobile owner is randomly selected, what is the probability that

>   1. He or she was involved in an accident during the past two years?
>   2. He or she lives in Community C?
>   3. He or she was involved in an accident during the last two years and lives in Community C?
>   4. He or she was not involved in an accident during the last two years or lives in Community A?

B. If an automobile owner was involved in an accident during the last two years, what is the probability he or she lives in Community A?

C. Is having an automobile accident during the last two years statistically independent of the community in which one lives?

SOLUTION

A.

  1. $P(Y) = 329/1500 = .219$

  2. $P(C) = 550/1500 = .367$

  3. By the formula for joint probability

$$
\begin{aligned}
P(Y \cap C) &= P(Y|C) \ \ P(C) \\
&= (164/550) \ \ (550/1500) \\
&= 164/1500 \\
&= .109
\end{aligned}
$$

   $P(Y \cap C)$ can also be found directly from the contingency table by dividing the number of people who live in Community C and had an accident during the last two years by the total number of automobile owners (i.e., $P(Y \cap C) = 164/1500 = .109$).

  4. $P(Y' \cup A)$
$$
\begin{aligned}
&= P(Y') + P(A) - P(Y' \cap A) \\
&= 1171/1500 + 450/1500 - 378/1500 \\
&= 1243/1500 \\
&= .829
\end{aligned}
$$

B. By the formula for conditional probability

$$ P(A|Y) = P(A \cap Y)/P(Y) $$

$$ = \frac{72/1500}{329/1500} $$

$$ = 72/329 $$
$$ = .219 $$

We could have solved this by first finding the automobile owners who had an accident during the last two years (329) and then finding the number of these who lived in Community A (72). The proportion 72/329 would give the number of automobile owners who had an accident during the last two years.

C. If P(A|B) = P(A), the two events are said to be statistically independent.

$$P(Y|A) = P(Y)$$
$$P(Y|A) = 72/450 = .16$$
$$P(Y) = 329/1500 = .219$$

Since P(Y|A) ≠ P(Y), these events are not statistically independent.

REVIEW PROBLEMS

I. Suppose that a survey has been undertaken to determine if there is a relationship between place of residence and ownership of a pet. A random sample of 100 individuals from large cities, 150 from suburbs, and 100 from rural areas was selected with the following results:

Pet Ownership	-----------------Type of Residence----------------			
	Rural	Suburb	Large City	Total
Owns a pet	80	115	50	245
Does not own a pet	20	35	50	105
Total	100	150	100	350

A. If an individual is selected at random, what is the probability that he or she:

1. owns a pet?

2. lives in a suburb?

3. owns a pet or lives in a large city?

4. lives in a large city or a suburb?

5. Are living in a large city or living in a suburb mutually exclusive events? Explain why or why not?

6. If an individual is selected at random, what is the probability that he or she lives in a large city and owns a pet?

7. Are these two events statistically independent? How do you know this?

8. If an individual is selected at random, what is the probability that he or she lives in a rural area or does not own a pet?

SOLUTION

Let $P(P)$ = owns a pet
          $P(P')$ = does not own a pet
          $P(R)$ = rural residence
          $P(S)$ = suburban residence
          $P(C)$ = city residence

1. $P(P)$ = 245/350 = .70

2. $P(S)$ = 150/350 = .43

3. $P(P \cup C)$ = $P(P) + P(C) - P(P \cap C)$
                  = 245/350 + 100/350 − 50/350
                  = 295/350 = .84

4. $P(C \cup S)$ = $P(C) + P(S) - 0$
   = $100/350 + 150/350$
   = $250/350$
   = $.714$

5. Yes. The intersection of these events is equal to zero.

6. $P(C \cap P)$ = $P(C|P)P(P)$
   = $(50/245) \ (245/350)$
   = $50/350$
   = $.14$

7. No. If $P(C|P) = P(C)$, then these events are statistically independent.

   $P(C|P)$ = $50/245$
   $P(C)$ = $100/350$
   $50/245$ ≠ $100/350$

   Therefore, these events are not statistically independent.

8. $P(R \cup P')$ = $P(R) + P(P') - P(R \cap P')$

   $$= \frac{100}{350} + \frac{105}{350} - \frac{20}{350}$$

   $$= \frac{185}{350}$$

   $$= .53$$

II. A businessman is trying to decide whether to invest money in a wildcat oil well. He knows that 10% of the time investors strike it rich, 60% of the time they break even, and 30% of the time they lose money. Before the businessman decides, he will study a geologist's report on the wells he is considering. In the past, 60% of the big oil strikes received a positive report, 50% of the break-even wells received a positive report, and 10% of the dry wells received positive reports.

A. Find the probability that the investor will strike it rich if the report is positive.

B. What is the probability of a positive report?

SOLUTION

A. Using Bayes' theorem we can find the probability that an investor will strike it rich if the report is positive.

Let

event S_1 = strikes it rich   event P = positive report
event S_2 = breaks even   event P' = negative report
event S_3 = loses

$$P(S_1|P) = \frac{P(P|S_1)P(S_1)}{P(P|S_1)P(S_1) + P(P|S_2)P(S_2) + P(P|S_3)P(S_3)}$$

$$= \frac{(.60)(.10)}{(.60)(.10) + (.50)(.60) + (.10)(.30)}$$

$$= \frac{.06}{.06 + .30 + .03}$$

$$= \frac{.06}{.39} = .15$$

B. The probability of a positive report P(P) is the sum of the joint probabilities.

$$P(P) = \sum_{i=1}^{n} P(P|S_i)P(S_i)$$

$$= P(P|S_1)P(S_1) + P(P|S_2)P(S_2) + P(P|S_3)P(S_3)$$

$$= .06 + .30 + .03$$

$$= .39$$

Events S_i	Prior Probability $P(S_i)$	Conditional Probability $P(P|S_i)$	Joint Probability $P(P|S_i)P(S_i)$	Revised Probability $P(S_i|P)$
S_1 = strike it rich	.10	.60	.06	.15
S_2 = breaks even	.60	.50	.30	.77
S_3 = loses	.30	.10	.03	.08
			$P(P) = \overline{.39}$	

III. Japanese businessmen often eat a very rare kind of raw fish. While the taste makes the risk worthwhile, 5% of the time people die from a toxin which may be present in the fish. The health department is required to check for this toxin; 90% of the good fish checked received a passing grade on the test, but 20% of the bad fish also received a passing grade.

    A. What is the probability that a person will receive "fatal fish" given that it received a passing grade by the health department?

B. What is the probability that the fish received a passing grade?

SOLUTION

A. Using Bayes' theorem we can find the probability that a businessman will receive "fatal fish" given that the health department gave it a passing grade.

Let

event	S = good fish	event P = passing grade
	S' = fatal fish	P' = failing grade

$$P(S'|P) = \frac{P(P|S') \, P(S')}{P(P|S') \, P(S') + P(P|S) \, P(S)}$$

$$= \frac{(.20) \, (.05)}{(.20) \, (.05) + (.90) \, (.95)}$$

$$= \frac{.01}{(.01) + (.86)}$$

$$= \frac{.01}{.87}$$

$$= .011$$

B. The probability that the fish received a passing grade P(P) is the sum of the joint probabilities.

$$P(P) = \sum_{i=1}^{n} P(P|S_i) \, P(S_i)$$

$$= P(P|S)P(S) + P(P|S')P(S')$$

$$= .86 + .01$$

$$= .87$$

Events S_i	Prior Probability $P(S_i)$	Conditional Probability $P(P|S_i)$	Joint Probability $P(P|S_i)P(S_i)$	Revised Probability $P(S_i|P)$
S = good fish	.95	.90	.86	.989
S ' = fatal fish	.05	.20	.01	.011
			.87	

7

Some Important Discrete Probability Distributions

In the previous chapter we established various rules of probability and examined some counting techniques. In this chapter we utilize this information to explore various probability models which represent certain phenomena of interest. In particular, the following discrete probability distributions are considered: the uniform distribution, the binomial distribution, the hypergeometric distribution, and the Poisson distribution. In addition, the concept of mathematical expectation is discussed.

MULTIPLE CHOICE

1. Whenever p=.5, the binomial distribution will be:

    a. symmetric
    b. symmetric if n is large
    c. highly right-skewed
    d. highly left-skewed

2. If n=10 and p=.70, then the mean of the binomial distribution is:

    a.   .07
    b.   1.45
    c.   7.00
    d. 14.29

3. If n=20 and p=.15, then P(X=4|n=20,p=.15) =

    a. .0005
    b. .1821
    c. .2428
    d. .8298

4. As a rule of thumb, when sampling without replacement you may use the binomial probability distribution to approximate the hypergeometric distribution whenever:

    a. the sample size is less than 5% of the population size.
    b. the sample size is at least 50% of the population size.
    c. n is very large and p is very small.
    d. the probability of success, p=.5.

5. The Poisson distribution may be used to approximate the binomial distribution for those situations in which:

    a. n is very small and p is very large.
    b. n is very large and p is very small.
    c. n is very large and p is very large.
    d. n is very small and p is very small.

6. When sample data are drawn without replacement from a finite population, the outcome of one observation is affected by the outcomes of the previous observations. Data obtained in this manner follow the:

    a. binomial model.
    b. Poisson distribution.
    c. normal distribution.
    d. hypergeometric distribution.

EXAMPLES

I. A Manhattan realty company summarized the number of apartments it rented per day for the last year (365 days) in the table below.

Number of Apartments Rented Per Day	Frequency of Occurrence
0	10
1	12
2	18
3	21
4	23
5	32
6	46
7	61
8	45
9	38
10	17
11	14
12	10
13	7
14	5
15	6
Total	365

A. Convert the observed frequencies in this table to probabilities for this 365 day period.

B. Calculate the expected number of apartment rentals per day.

C. Calculate the standard deviation of this probability distribution.

D. What is the probability that on any given day:

    1. fewer than 5 apartments will be rented?
    2. at most 5 apartments will be rented?
    3. at least 5 apartments will be rented?
    4. exactly 5 apartments will be rented?
    5. more than 5 apartments will be rented?

SOLUTION

A.

Number of Apartments Rented Per Day (X_i)	Frequency of Occurrence	Probability $P(X_i)$	$(X_i)P(X_i)$
0	10	0.027	0.000
1	12	0.033	0.033
2	18	0.049	0.098
3	21	0.058	0.174
4	23	0.063	0.252
5	32	0.088	0.440
6	46	0.126	0.756
7	61	0.167	1.169
8	45	0.123	0.984
9	38	0.104	0.936
10	17	0.047	0.470
11	14	0.038	0.418
12	10	0.027	0.324
13	7	0.019	0.247
14	5	0.014	0.196
15	6	0.016	0.240
Totals	365	1.000	6.737

$$\sum_{i=1}^{N} X_i P(X_i)$$

B. $\mu_x = E(X) = \sum_{i=1}^{N} X_i P(X_i)$

$= (0)\,(0.027) + (1)\,(0.033) + (2)\,(0.049) + (3)\,(0.058)$
$+ \ldots + (15)\,(0.016)$

$= 6.74$

C.

Number of Apartments Rented Per Day	$(X_i - \mu_x)$	$(X_i - \mu_x)^2$	$(X_i - \mu_x)^2 P(X_i)$
0	−6.74	45.43	1.23
1	−5.74	32.95	1.09
2	−4.74	22.47	1.10
3	−3.74	13.99	0.81
4	−2.74	7.51	0.47
5	−1.74	3.03	0.27
6	− .74	.55	0.07
7	.26	.07	0.01
8	1.26	1.59	0.20
9	2.26	5.11	0.53
10	3.26	10.63	0.50
11	4.26	18.15	0.69
12	5.26	27.67	0.75
13	6.26	39.19	0.74
14	7.26	52.71	0.74
15	8.26	68.23	1.09
Totals			10.29

$$\sum_{i=1}^{N} (X_i - \mu_x)^2 P(X_i)$$

$$\sigma_x = \sqrt{\sum_{i=1}^{n} (X_i - \mu_x)^2 \, P(X_i)}$$

$$= \sqrt{10.29}$$

$$= 3.21$$

D. (1)   P(X < 5)   = P(X = 0) + P(X = 1) + P(X = 2) + P(X = 3) + P(X = 4)

                        = 0.027 + 0.033 + 0.049 + 0.058 + 0.063

                        = 0.230

   (2)   P(X ≤ 5)   = P(X = 0) + P(X = 1) + P(X = 2) + P(X = 3) + P(X = 4)
                          + P(X = 5)

                        = 0.027 + 0.033 + 0.049 + 0.058 + 0.063 + 0.088

                        = 0.318

   (3)   P(X ≥ 5)   = P(X = 5) + P(X = 6) + P(X = 7) + ... + P(X = 15)

                        = 0.088 + 0.126 + 0.167 + ... + 0.016

                        = 0.769

   (4)   P(X = 5)   = 0.088

   (5)   P(X > 5)   = P(X = 6) + P(X = 7) + P(X = 8) + ... + P(X = 15)

                        = 0.126 + 0.167 + 0.123 + ... + 0.016

                        = 0.681

II. A box of 8 ceramic mugs contains one slightly marred mug. If you select three mugs at random without replacement, find the probability that

    a. none of the three is marred.
    b. one of the three is marred.
    c. If the sample had been drawn with replacement, what would your answers be to (a) and (b)?

SOLUTION

Parts (a) and (b) are examples using the hypergeometric distribution:

$$P(X{=}x|n,N,A) = \frac{\binom{A}{X}\binom{N-A}{n-X}}{\binom{N}{n}}$$

where

    n = the sample size = 3
    N = the population size = 8
    A = the number of good mugs in the population = 7
    X = the number of good mugs in the sample
    $N{-}A$ = the number of marred mugs in the population = 1

(a) $P(X{=}3|n{=}3,N{=}8,A{=}7) = \dfrac{\binom{7}{3}\binom{1}{0}}{\binom{8}{3}} = \dfrac{\frac{7!}{3!4!}(1)}{\frac{8!}{3!5!}} = \dfrac{35}{56} = .625$

(b) $P(X{=}2|n{=}3,N{=}8,A{=}7) = \dfrac{\binom{7}{2}\binom{1}{1}}{\binom{8}{3}} = \dfrac{\frac{7!}{2!5!}(1)}{\frac{8!}{3!5!}} = \dfrac{21}{56} = .375$

(c) If a mug is replaced before the next draw, the proportion of good mugs is constant for each draw. Therefore, we have a binomial distribution problem. (Use Table E.7.)

    (1) $P(X{=}3|n{=}3,p{=}.88) = \dfrac{3!}{3!0!}(.88)^3\ (.12)^0 = .6815$

    (2) $P(X{=}2|n{=}3,p{=}.88) = \dfrac{3!}{2!1!}(.88)^2\ (.12)^1 = .2788$

III. The probability that an insurance agent will sell a life-insurance policy to someone who has been randomly selected from the telephone directory is .15. If an insurance agent calls 6 persons, what is the probability that he will sell:

A. 1. no policies
2. exactly 3 policies
3. at most 3 policies
4. at least 4 policies

B. If we increase the number of calls from n=5 to n=50, what would be the expected number of sales?

SOLUTION

A. This is an example of the binomial probability distribution:

$$P(X=x|n,p) = \frac{n!}{x! \ (n-x)!} \ p^x \ (1-p)^{n-x}$$

where

n = the number of persons called
X = the number of policies sold
p = probability of selling a life insurance policy
$1-p$ = probability of no sale

1. $P(X=0) = \dfrac{6!}{0!6!} \ (.15)^0 \ (.85)^6 = (1) \ (1) \ (.3771) = .3771$

2. $P(X=3) = \dfrac{6!}{3!3!} \ (.15)^3 \ (.85)^3 = (20) \ (.0034) \ (.6141) = .0418$

3. $P(X \leq 3) = P(X=0) + P(X=1) + P(X=2) + P(X=3)$

$$= .3771 + \frac{6!}{1!5!} \ (.15)^1 \ (.85)^5 + \frac{6!}{2!4!} \ (.15)^2 \ (.85)^4 + .0418$$

$$= .3771 + (6) \ (.15) \ (.4437) + (15) \ (.0225) \ (.5220) + .0418$$

$$= .3771 + .3993 + .1762 + .0418$$

$$= .9944$$

4. $P(X \geq 4) = P(X=4) + P(X=5) + P(X=6)$

$$= \frac{6!}{4!2!} (.15)^4 (.85)^2 + \frac{6!}{5!1!} (.15)^5 (.85)^1 + \frac{6!}{6!0!} (.15)^6 (.85)^0$$

$$= (15) (.0005) (.7225) + (6) (.0001) (.85) + (1) (.0000) (1)$$

$$= .0054 + .0005 + .0000$$

$$= .0059$$

B. $\mu_x = E(X) = np = (50) (.15) = 7.5$

On the average, he may expect to make a sale 7.5 times when he calls on 50 people.

IV. On the average the emergency room at Community Hospital admits 5 persons per hour for injuries suffered in automobile accidents. What is the probability that:

a. exactly three persons will be admitted to the hospital for injuries from automobile accidents during a randomly selected hour?
b. fewer than three persons will be admitted for injuries from automobile accidents during a randomly selected hour?
c. three or more persons will be admitted for injuries from automobile accidents during a randomly selected hour?

SOLUTION

Poisson Distribution:

$$P(X=x|\lambda) = \frac{e^{-\lambda}\lambda^x}{x!}$$

where $\lambda = 5$
X = number of patients admitted for automobile accidents

(a) $P(X=3|\lambda=5) = \dfrac{e^{-5}5^3}{3!} = .1404$

(b) $P(X\leq2)$ $= P(X=0) + P(X=1) + P(X=2)$

$$= \frac{e^{-5}5^0}{0!} + \frac{e^{-5}5^1}{1!} + \frac{e^{-5}5^2}{2!}$$

$$= .0067 + .0337 + .0842$$

$$= .1246$$

(c) $P(X\geq3|\lambda=5) = 1 - \{P(X=0|\lambda=5) + P(X=1|\lambda=5) + P(X=2|\lambda=5)\}$

$$= 1 - \left\{\frac{e^{-5}5^0}{0!} + \frac{e^{-5}5^1}{1!} + \frac{e^{-5}5^2}{2!}\right\}$$

$$= 1 - (.0067 + .0337 + .0842)$$

$$= 1 - (.1246)$$

$$= .8754$$

There is approximately a 12.46% chance that two or fewer automobile victims will be admitted to Community Hospital, so there is an 87.54% chance that three or more persons will be admitted for automobile accidents.

REVIEW PROBLEMS

I. A magazine publisher is using a sweepstakes gimmick to promote sales. The publisher mailed an official entry blank to 10,000 prospective subscribers indicating that the number appearing on their entry made them eligible to win one of the following prizes:

Prizes	Value of Prizes	Number of Prizes
Ten Thousand Dollars	$10,000.00	1
Television Set	$550.00	10
Camera	$35.00	50
Pocket Calculator	$5.00	300
Pen and Pencil Set	$2.00	1,000
Calendar	$.25	8,639

A. Form the probability distribution for the prizes that an entrant can win.

B. Compute the expected value of entering these sweepstakes.

C. Compute the variance and standard deviation.

SOLUTION

A.

Prizes	Value of Prizes X_i	Number of Prizes	Probability $P(X_i)$
Ten Thousand Dollars	$10,000.00	1	.0001
Television Set	$550.00	10	.0010
Camera	$35.00	50	.0050
Pocket Calculator	$5.00	300	.0300
Pen and Pencil Set	$2.00	1,000	.1000
Calendar	$.25	8,639	.8639
		10,000	1.0000

B. and C.

Value (X_i)	$P(X_i)$	$X_iP(X_i)$	$(X_i - \mu_X)$	$(X_i - \mu_X)^2$	$(X_i - \mu_X)^2 P(X_i)$
$10,000.00	.0001	1.000	9997.71	99954205.24	9,995.42
$550.00	.0010	.550	547.71	299986.24	299.99
$35.00	.0050	.175	32.71	1069.94	5.35
$5.00	.0300	.150	2.71	7.34	.22
$2.00	.1000	.200	−.29	.08	.01
$.25	.8639	.216	−2.04	4.16	3.59
		2.291			10,304.58

B. Expected Value: $\mu_X = E(X) = \sum_{i=1}^{N} X_i\, P(X_i) = \$2.29$

C. Variance: $\sigma_X^2 = \text{Var}(X) = \sum_{i=1}^{N}(X_i - \mu_x)^2\, P(X_i) = 10{,}304.58$

D. Standard Deviation: $\sigma_X = \sqrt{\text{Var}(X)} = \sqrt{10{,}304.58} = \$101.51$

II. The Nakata Corporation has determined that 10% of the pocket calculators manufactured at its main plant are defective. If a random sample of 70 is selected, what is the probability that:

    (a) five of the calculators will be defective?
    (b) at least two of the calculators will be defective?
    (c) no more than four of the calculators will be defective?

SOLUTION

This is an example using the Poisson as an approximation of the binomial distribution when n is large and p is small.

$$P(X=x|n,p) \cong \frac{e^{-np}\,(np)^x}{x!}$$

    where

        n = the sample size = 70
        p = the true probability of a defective calculator
        e = 2.71828 (the base of the natural logarithmic system)
        X = the number of defective calculators in the sample

(a) $P(X=5|n=70,p=.10) \cong \dfrac{e^{-7}7^5}{5!} = .1277$

(b) $P(X\geq2|n=70,p=.10) \cong 1 - \{P(X=0) + P(X=1)\}$

$$= 1 - \left\{\dfrac{e^{-7}7^0}{0!} + \dfrac{e^{-7}7^1}{1!}\right\}$$

$$= 1 - (.0009 + .0064)$$

$$= 1 - .0073$$

$$= .9927$$

(c) $P(X\leq4|n=70,p=.10) \cong P(X=0) + P(X=1) + P(X=2) + P(X=3) + P(X=4)$

$$= .0009 + .0064 + \dfrac{e^{-7}7^2}{2!} + \dfrac{e^{-7}7^3}{3!} + \dfrac{e^{-7}7^4}{4!}$$

$$= .0009 + .0064 + .0223 + .0521 + .0912$$

$$= .1729$$

III. In a jewelry store, a display case showing 12 watches contains 2 watches with defective clasps. If a customer purchases 3 watches, what is the probability that:

(a) exactly one has a defective clasp?
(b) none has a defective clasp?

SOLUTION

Hypergeometric Distribution:

$$P(X=x|n,N,A) = \frac{\binom{A}{x}\binom{N-A}{n-x}}{\binom{N}{n}}$$

where

N=12, A=2, n=3, and X=number of watches with defective clasps

(a) $P(X=1) = \dfrac{\binom{2}{1}\binom{10}{2}}{\binom{12}{3}} = \dfrac{\left(\frac{2!}{1!1!}\right)\left(\frac{10!}{2!8!}\right)}{\left(\frac{12!}{3!9!}\right)} = \dfrac{(2)\,(45)}{220} = .409$

(b) $P(X=0) = \dfrac{\binom{2}{0}\binom{10}{3}}{\binom{12}{3}} = \dfrac{\left(\frac{2!}{0!2!}\right)\left(\frac{10!}{3!7!}\right)}{\left(\frac{12!}{3!9!}\right)}$

$$= \frac{(1)\,(120)}{220}$$

$$= .545$$

IV. The sound system for a rock group works properly 75% of the time.

   A. What is the probability that in 8 system checks it is operating properly:

      1. exactly 3 times?
      2. at least 5 times?
      3. at most 2 times?
      4. more than 6 times?

   B. How many times can the system be expected to work properly?

SOLUTION

A. This is an example of the binomial probability distribution:

$$P(X=x|n,p) = \frac{n!}{x! \, (n-x)!} \, p^x \, (1-p)^{n-x}$$

where

n = the number of system checks
X = the number of times it works properly
p = the proportion of times the system works properly = .75
$1-p$ = the proportion of times the system does not work properly
= .25

(1) $P(X=3) = \dfrac{8!}{3! \, 5!} \, (.75)^3 \, (.25)^5 = (56) \, (.4219) \, (.0010)$

$= .0236$

(2) $P(X \geq 5) = \dfrac{8!}{5! \, 3!} \, (.75)^5 \, (.25)^3 + \dfrac{8!}{6! \, 2!} \, (.75)^6 \, (.25)^2$

$+ \dfrac{8!}{7! \, 1!} \, (.75)^7 \, (.25)^1 + \dfrac{8!}{8! \, 0!} \, (.75)^8 \, (.25)^0$

$$= (56) \ (.2373) \ (.0156) + (28) \ (.1780) \ (.0625)$$
$$+ \ (8) \ (.1335) \ (.25) + (1) \ (.1001) \ (1)$$

$$= .2073 + .3115 + .2670 + .1001$$

$$= .8859$$

(3) $P(X \le 2) = P(X=0) + P(X=1) + P(X=2)$

$$= \frac{8!}{0!8!} \ (.75)^0 \ (.25)^8 + \frac{8!}{1!7!} \ (.75)^1 \ (.25)^7 + \frac{8!}{2!6!} \ (.75)^2 \ (.25)^6$$

$$= (1) \ (1) \ (.0000) + (8) \ (.75) \ (.0001) + (28) \ (.5625) \ (.0002)$$

$$= .0000 + .0006 + .0032$$

$$= .0038$$

(4) $P(X > 6) = P(X=7) + P(X=8)$

$$= \frac{8!}{7!1!} \ (.75)^7 \ (.25)^1 + \frac{8!}{8!0!} \ (.75)^8 \ (.25)^0$$

$$= (8) \ (.1335) \ (.25) + (1) \ (.1001) \ (1)$$

$$= .2670 + .1001$$

$$= .3671$$

B. $\mu_x = E(X) = np = (8) \ (.75) = 6$

On the average, we can expect the system to work properly six times.

8

The Normal Distribution

The normal distribution is the most important of the continuous probability models. In this chapter the normal distribution is described not only for its representation of numerous continuous phenomena, but also for its use in approximating discrete probability distributions (such as the uniform, binomial, hypergeometric, and Poisson) in an effort to save computational drudgery. Such concepts as finite population correction factor and the correction for continuity adjustment are also discussed.

MULTIPLE CHOICE

1. Which of the following is *not* theoretically true about the normal distribution.

   a. It is "bell-shaped" and symmetrical in appearance.
   b. Its measures of central tendency (mean, median, mode, midrange, and midhinge) are all identical.
   c. Its "middle spread" is equal to 1.33 standard deviations.
   d. Its associated random variable has a finite range.

2. The exact form of a normal distribution is determined by the:

    a. population mean.
    b. population standard deviation.
    c. population mean, standard deviation, and lambda.
    d. a and b.

3. How do the normal distributions below differ?

    a. different means
    b. different standard deviations
    c. different means and standard deviations
    d. different areas under the curve

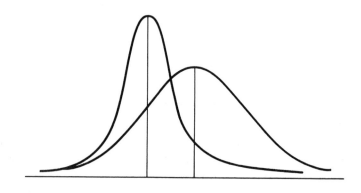

4. A _____ always has a mean $\mu_Z = 0$ and a standard deviation $\sigma_Z = 1$.

    a. normal distribution
    b. standardized normal distribution
    c. continuous probability distribution
    d. discrete probability distribution

5. Probabilities, proportions, and areas under a curve must always add up to _____.

    a. 0.000
    b. 0.001
    c. 0.999
    d. 1.000

6. If Y is the highest point on a normal curve, then X must equal

    a. zero.
    b. one.
    c. the mean.
    d. the standard deviation.

7. In a normal distribution, 68.26% of the data are contained within the limits

    a. $\mu_x \pm 0.50\sigma_x$.
    b. $\mu_x \pm 0.68\sigma_x$.
    c. $\mu_x \pm 1.00\sigma_x$.
    d. $\mu_x \pm 1.96\sigma_x$.

8. The normal distribution may be used to approximate the

    a. binomial model.
    b. hypergeometric model.
    c. Poisson model.
    d. All of the above.

9. The correction for continuity adjustment requires the adding or subtracting of _____ from the value or values of the discrete random variable X as needed.

    a. μ_x
    b. σ_x
    c. (n) (p)
    d. 0.5

10. The normal distribution can be used to approximate the binomial distribution if:

    a. (n) (p) = 0.5.
    b. (n) (p) ≥ 5.0.
    c. n(1-p) ≥ 5.0.
    d. Both b and c must hold.

EXAMPLES

I. The number of days between placing an order for a book and receiving the book is normally distributed with a mean of 30 days and a standard deviation of 5 days.

   (a) What proportion of books will be received between 30 and 37 days?
   (b) What proportion of books will be received between 15 and 35 days?
   (c) What proportion of books will be received between 37 and 39 days?
   (d) How many days pass when all but 5% of the books have been received?

SOLUTION

  (a) $P(30 \leq X \leq 37) = ?$

$$Z = \frac{X - \mu_x}{\sigma_x} = \frac{37 - 30}{5} = \frac{7}{5} = 1.40$$

$P(30 \leq X \leq 37) = .4192$ or 41.92%

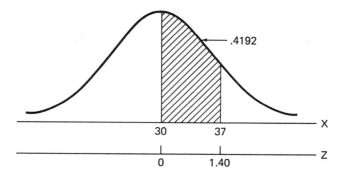

  (b) $P(15 \leq X \leq 35) = ?$

$$Z = \frac{15 - 30}{5} = \frac{-15}{5} = -3.00$$

$$Z = \frac{35 - 30}{5} = \frac{5}{5} = 1.00$$

$$P(15 \leq X \leq 35) = .49865 + .3413$$
$$= .83995 \text{ or } 83.995\%$$

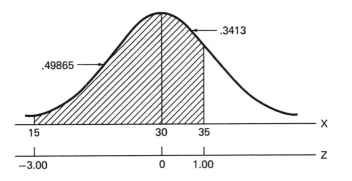

(c) $P(37 \leq X \leq 39) = ?$

$$Z = \frac{37 - 30}{5} = \frac{7}{5} = 1.40$$

$$Z = \frac{39 - 30}{5} = \frac{9}{5} = 1.80$$

$$\begin{aligned} P(37 \leq X \leq 39) &= .4641 - .4192 \\ &= .0449 \text{ or } 4.49\% \end{aligned}$$

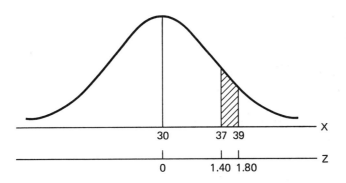

(d) Computation of days which pass when all but 5.0% of the books have been received.

$$Z = \frac{X - \mu_x}{\sigma_x} \quad \text{or} \quad 1.65 = \frac{X - 30}{5}$$

$$\begin{aligned} X - 30 &= 1.65(5) \\ X &= 30 + 8.25 \\ X &= 38.25 \text{ days} \end{aligned}$$

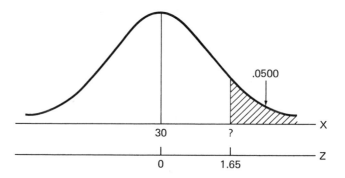

II. The amount of coffee served daily at a commuter railroad station is normally distributed with a mean of 3000 ounces and a standard deviation of 190 ounces. What percentage of the time does the coffee shop serve:

  (a) between 3000 ounces and 3370 ounces of coffee?
  (b) between 2540 ounces and 3291 ounces of coffee?
  (c) more than 3372 ounces of coffee?
  (d) less than 2628 ounces of coffee?
  (e) between 2628 ounces and 3372 ounces of coffee?

SOLUTION

  (a) $P(3000 \leq X \leq 3370) = ?$

$$Z = \frac{X - \mu_x}{\sigma_x} = \frac{3370 - 3000}{190}$$

$$= \frac{370}{190} = 1.95$$

$$P(3000 \leq X \leq 3370) = .4744$$
$$\text{or } 47.44\%$$

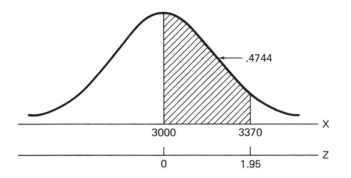

(b) P(2540 ≤ X ≤ 3291) = ?

$$Z = \frac{2540 - 3000}{190} = \frac{-460}{190} = -2.42$$

$$Z = \frac{3291 - 3000}{190} = \frac{291}{190} = 1.53$$

P(2540 ≤ X ≤ 3291) = .4922 + .4370
= .9292 or 92.92%

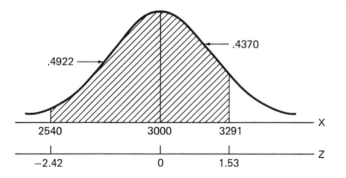

(c) P(X > 3372) = ?

$$Z = \frac{3372 - 3000}{190} = \frac{372}{190} = 1.96$$

P(X ≥ 3372) = .5000 − .4750 = .0250
or 2.5%

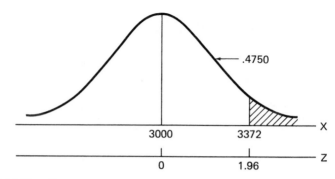

(d) $P(X \le 2628) = ?$

$$Z = \frac{2628 - 3000}{190} = \frac{-372}{190} = -1.96$$

$$P(X \le 2628) = .5000 - .4750 = .0250$$
$$\text{or } 2.5\%$$

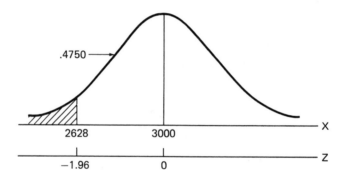

(e) $P(2628 \le X \le 3372) = ?$

$$P(2628 \le X \le 3372) = .4750 + .4750$$
$$= .9500$$
$$\text{or } 95\%$$

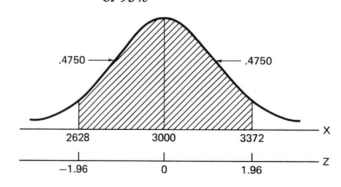

III. A sample of n=1500 cans of paint are randomly obtained from an ongoing process in which 6.0% of these cans are mismatched for the requested color of paint. What is the probability that:

(a) no more than 100 cans of paint will be mismatched?
(b) exactly 100 cans of paint will be mismatched?

SOLUTION

Normal Approximation to the Binomial: μ_x $= np = (1500)\,(.06) = 90$

$$\sigma_x \ = \sqrt{np(1-p)}$$

$$= \sqrt{(90)\,(.94)}$$

$$= \sqrt{84.6}$$

$$= 9.20$$

(a) $Z = \dfrac{X - np}{\sqrt{np(1-p)}} = \dfrac{100.5 - 90}{9.20} = \dfrac{10.5}{9.20} = 1.14$

$P(X \leq 100) = .5000 + .3729 = .8729$

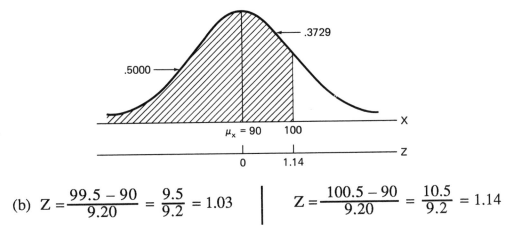

(b) $Z = \dfrac{99.5 - 90}{9.20} = \dfrac{9.5}{9.2} = 1.03$ $\Big|$ $Z = \dfrac{100.5 - 90}{9.20} = \dfrac{10.5}{9.2} = 1.14$

$P(X = 100) = .3729 - .3485 = .0244$

REVIEW PROBLEM

I. The average annual bonus for employees of a particular company is $1800 with a standard deviation of $75. Assuming that the bonuses are normally distributed, what percentage of the bonuses are:

(a) between $1681.50 and $1800.00?

(b) between $1675.50 and $1924.50?

(c) between $1606.50 and $1700.25?

(d) less than $1725.00?

(e) more than $1993.50?

(f) less than $1703.25 or more than $1896.75?

(g) What is the value of a bonus if only 25% of the employees in this company receive more than that amount?

(h) What is the value of a bonus if only 15% of the employees in this company receive less than that amount?

SOLUTION

$\mu_X = \$1800.00 \qquad \sigma_X = \$75.00$

(a) $Z = \dfrac{1681.50 - 1800.00}{75.00} = \dfrac{-118.50}{75.00} = -1.58$

$P(1681.50 \leq X \leq 1800.00) = .4429$ or 44.29%

(b) $Z = \dfrac{1675.50 - 1800.00}{75.00} = \dfrac{-124.50}{75.00} = -1.66$

$Z = \dfrac{1924.50 - 1800.00}{75.00} = \dfrac{124.50}{75.00} = 1.66$

$P(1675.50 \leq X \leq 1924.50) = .4515 + .4515 = .9030$ or 90.30%

(c) $Z = \dfrac{1606.50{-}1800.00}{75.00} = \dfrac{-193.5}{75.00} = -2.58$

$Z = \dfrac{1700.25{-}1800.00}{75.00} = \dfrac{-99.75}{75.00} = -1.33$

$P(1606.50 \leq X \leq 1700.25) = .4951 - .4082 = .0869$ or 8.69%

(d) $Z = \dfrac{1725.00 - 1800.00}{75.00} = \dfrac{-75.00}{75.00} = -1.00$

$P(X < 1725) = .5000 - .3413 = .1587$ or 15.87%

(e) $Z = \dfrac{1993.50 - 1800.00}{75.00} = \dfrac{193.50}{75.00} = 2.58$

$P(X > 1993.50) = .5000 - .4951 = .0049$ or .49%

(f) $Z = \dfrac{1703.25{-}1800.00}{75.00} = \dfrac{-96.75}{75.00} = -1.29$

$Z = \dfrac{1896.75{-}1800.00}{75.00} = \dfrac{96.75}{75.00} = 1.29$

$$P(X \leq 1703.25 \text{ or } X \geq 1896.75) = 1 - (.4015 + .4015)$$
$$= 1 - .8030$$
$$= .1970 \text{ or } 19.70\%$$

(g) $+.67 = \dfrac{X - 1800.00}{75.00}$

$X - 1800.00 = (.67)\,(75)$
$X - 1800.00 = 50.25$
$X = \$1850.25$

(h) $-1.04 = \dfrac{X - 1800.00}{75.00}$

$X - 1800.00 = (-1.04)\,(75.00)$
$X - 1800.00 = 78.00$
$X = \$1722.00$

9

Sampling Distributions

One of the major goals of statistical analysis is to use a sample statistic such as the average to estimate a true population value. In order to be able to perform the analysis, we need to know the shape of the distribution of all possible samples. When the population is normally distributed, the sampling distribution of the mean will also be normally distributed with a variability that will decrease as the sample size becomes larger. On the other hand, if the population is "other than normally distributed," from the Central Limit Theorem we observe that once the sample size is large enough, the distribution of the sample mean will also follow a normal distribution.

MULTIPLE CHOICE

1. According to the central limit theorem, the sampling distribution of the mean can be approximated by the normal distribution

   a. as the number of samples gets "large enough."
   b. as the sample size (number of observations in each sample) gets large enough.
   c. as the size of the population standard deviation increases.
   d. as the size of the sample standard deviation decreases.

2. When we show that _____, we are demonstrating the property of unbiasedness.

   a. $\mu_x = \mu_{\overline{x}}$
   b. $\sigma_{\overline{x}} = \sigma_x/\sqrt{n}$
   c. $Z = (X - \mu_x)/\sigma_x$
   d. $Z = (\overline{X} - \mu_x)/(\sigma_x/\sqrt{n})$

3. The standard deviation of the sampling distribution of the mean is called the

   a. standard error of the sample.
   b. standard error of variability.
   c. standard error of the estimate.
   d. standard error of the mean.

4. If a sample of n=100 is drawn from a population whose standard deviation $\sigma_x = 100$, then the standard error of the mean equals

   a. 10
   b. 100
   c. 1000
   d. 10000

5. If we wanted to reduce the standard error of the mean in question #4 to 1.0, we would

    a. increase the sample size to 1,000.
    b. increase the sample size to 10,000.
    c. decrease the sample size to 50.
    d. decrease the sample size to 10.

6. When we show that the variation of the sample mean from the population mean decreases as the sample size increases, we are demonstrating the property of

    a. unbiasedness.
    b. efficiency.
    c. consistency.
    d. normality.

7. The law of large numbers explains why

    a. more sample means than individual population values lie closer to the population mean.
    b. the standard error of the mean is smaller than the population standard deviation.
    c. the standard error of the mean decreases as the sample size increases.
    d. All of the above.

8. The sampling distribution of the mean is a distribution of _____.

    a. individual population values.
    b. individual sample values.
    c. statistics.
    d. parameters.

9. The concept of a sampling distribution

    a. is essential for drawing conclusions about a population from the results of a sample.
    b. is related to the use of probability theory in inferential statistics.
    c. helps us use statistics to estimate the corresponding true values in the population.
    d. All of the above.

10. According to the central limit theorem, the sampling distribution of the mean will be approximately normally distributed for most populations, regardless of their shape, if

    a. at least 30 samples are selected.
    b. samples of at least 30 observations are selected.
    c. at least 500 samples are selected.
    d. at least 500 samples with 10 observations in each are selected.

EXAMPLES

I. In order to demonstrate the concept of the sampling distribution of the mean, a professor used the following example. A population of four questionnaires (A, B, C, and D) was checked for coding errors. The number of errors in each questionnaire was:

Questionnaire	Number of Errors
A	5
B	7
C	8
D	10

Samples of two questionnaires were selected without replacement from this population. The possible sample outcomes are shown in the table below.

Sample	Questionnaires	Sample Outcomes	Sample Mean $\bar{X}_i$
1	A,B	5,7	_____
2	A,C	5,8	_____
3	A,D	5,10	_____
4	B,C	7,8	_____
5	B,D	7,10	_____
6	C,D	8,10	_____

A. Calculate the population mean, μ_X.

B. Calculate the population standard deviation, σ_X.

C. Complete the last column in the table by computing the mean for each sample.

D. Demonstrate that the property of unbiasedness holds for this example.

E. Compare the variability of individual population values with the variability of sample means. How can you explain the differences in variability?

SOLUTION

A. $\mu_X = \dfrac{\sum\limits_{i\text{-}1}^{N} X_i}{N} = \dfrac{30}{4} = 7.5$ errors

B. $\sigma_X = \sqrt{\dfrac{\sum\limits_{i=1}^{N}(X_i - \mu_X)^2}{N}} = \sqrt{\dfrac{13}{4}} = \sqrt{3.25} = 1.803$ errors

C. $\overline{X}_1 = 6.0$

$\overline{X}_2 = 6.5$

$\overline{X}_3 = 7.5$

$\overline{X}_4 = 7.5$

$\overline{X}_5 = 8.5$

$\overline{X}_6 = 9.0$

D. μ_X = 7.5 errors

$$\mu_{\bar{x}} = \frac{6.0 + 6.5 + 7.5 + 7.5 + 8.5 + 9.0}{6}$$

$$= \frac{45.0}{6} = 7.5 \text{ errors}$$

Since $\mu_X = \mu_{\bar{x}}$ the property of unbiasedness holds.

E. There is less variability in sample means than in individual population values. The law of large numbers explains this difference. That is, while a population may contain individual values ranging from extremely small to extremely large, a particular sample mean averages together all the values in the sample. If a sample does include an extreme value, the effect of this extreme value on the mean will be reduced when it is averaged in with other values in the sample. As the sample size gets larger, the effect of any one value in the sample gets smaller.

II. The values of the accounts receivable for a department store are normally distributed with a population mean of μ_x = $260.00 and a standard deviation of σ_X = $15.00.

(a) What proportion of accounts receivable are between $250.00 and $260.00?
(b) What proportion of accounts receivable are between $248.00 and $268.00?
(c) If an auditor takes many random samples of size n=16 from this population of accounts receivable:

1. What would the mean be expected to equal?
2. What would the standard error of the mean be expected to equal?
3. What distribution would the sample means follow?
4. What proportion of the sample means would be between $250.00 and $260.00?
5. What proportion of the sample means would be between $248.00 and $268.00?

(d) Compare the answers to (a) with (c.4) or (b) with (c.5) and explain the differences.

(e) If samples of size n=16 are selected, within what limits will 95% of the sample means fall?

(f) If samples of size n=16 are selected, what average amount of accounts receivable will be exceeded by 75% of the sample means?

(g) If the samples are selected from a population of 200 accounts, find the standard error of the mean and the proportion of sample means between $250.00 and $260.00.

SOLUTION

Normal distribution of values of accounts receivable for a department store:

$$\mu_x = \$260.00, \quad \sigma_x = \$15.00$$

(a) $P(\$250.00 \leq X \leq \$260.00) = ?$

$$Z = \frac{X - \mu_x}{\sigma_x} = \frac{250 - 260}{15} = \frac{-10}{15} = -.67$$

$$P(250.00 \leq X \leq 260.00) = .2486$$

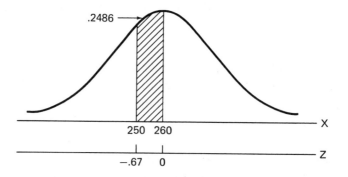

(b) $P(248.00 \leq X \leq 268.00) = ?$

$$Z = \frac{248.00 - 260.00}{15} = \frac{-12}{15} = -.80$$

$$Z = \frac{268.00 - 260.00}{15} = \frac{8}{15} = .53$$

$$P(248.00 \leq X \leq 268.00) = .2881 + .2019 = .4900$$

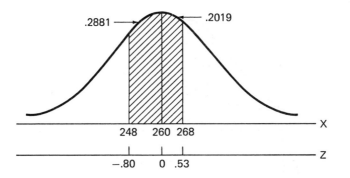

(c. 1 & 2)

If many random samples of 16 accounts receivable are selected, the average of all the sample means ($\mu_{\bar{x}}$) is the population mean (μ_x), and the standard deviation of all the sample means ($\sigma_{\bar{x}}$) is the population standard deviation (σ_x) divided by the square root of the sample size. Therefore, $\mu_{\bar{x}} = \mu_x = \$260.00$

and $\sigma_{\bar{x}} = \dfrac{\sigma_x}{\sqrt{n}} = \dfrac{15}{\sqrt{16}} = \$3.75.$

(c.3)

If the samples are selected from a normal population, the distribution of means follows a normal distribution, with mean, $\mu_{\bar{x}}$ and standard deviation $\sigma_{\bar{x}} = \dfrac{\sigma_x}{\sqrt{n}}$.

(c.4) $P(250.0 \leq \bar{X} \leq 260.00) = ?$

$$Z = \frac{\bar{X} - \mu_{\bar{x}}}{\dfrac{\sigma_x}{\sqrt{n}}} = \frac{250.00 - 260.00}{\dfrac{15}{\sqrt{16}}} = \frac{-10}{3.75} = -2.67$$

$P(250.00 \leq \bar{X} \leq 260.00) = .4962$

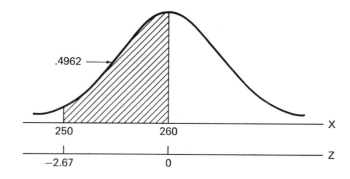

(c.5)   P(248.00 ≤ $\overline{X}$ ≤ 268.00) = ?

$$Z = \frac{248.00 - 260.00}{\dfrac{15}{\sqrt{16}}} = \frac{-12}{3.75} = -3.2$$

$$Z = \frac{268.00 - 260.00}{\dfrac{15}{\sqrt{16}}} = \frac{8}{3.75} = 2.13$$

P(248.00 ≤ $\overline{X}$ ≤ 268.00) = .49931 + .4834 = .98271

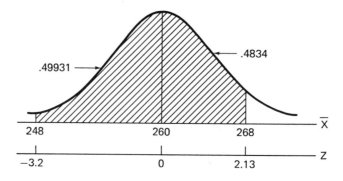

(d) The proportion of accounts receivable that are between \$250.00 and \$260.00 (.2486) or between \$248.00 and \$268.00 (.4900) is less than the proportion of sample means that are between \$250.00 and \$260.00 (.4962) or between \$248.00 and \$268.00 (.98271), since the sample means are less variable than the population data itself (i.e., $\sigma_X = 15$, whereas $\sigma_{\overline{X}} = \dfrac{\sigma_X}{\sqrt{n}} = 3.75$).

$$-Z_L = \frac{\overline{X}_L - \mu_x}{\dfrac{\sigma_x}{\sqrt{n}}} \qquad \text{and} \qquad Z_U = \frac{\overline{X}_U - \mu_x}{\dfrac{\sigma_x}{\sqrt{n}}}$$

Therefore,

$$\overline{X}_L = \mu_x - Z_L \left(\frac{\sigma_x}{\sqrt{n}}\right) \qquad\qquad \overline{X}_U = \mu_x + Z_U \left(\frac{\sigma_x}{\sqrt{n}}\right)$$

$$= 260 - 1.96 \left(\frac{15}{\sqrt{16}}\right) \qquad\qquad = 260 + 1.96 \left(\frac{15}{\sqrt{16}}\right)$$

$$= 260 - 7.35 \qquad\qquad\qquad\qquad = 260 + 7.35$$

$$= \$252.65 \qquad\qquad\qquad\qquad\quad = \$267.35$$

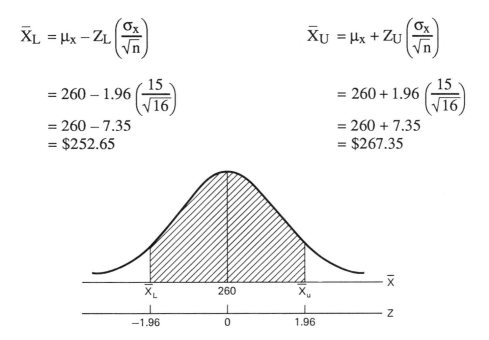

95% of all sample means of size 16 will fall between $252.65 and $267.35.

(f) Average amount of accounts receivable that will be exceeded by 75% of the sample means:

$$Z = \frac{\overline{X} - \mu_x}{\sigma_{\overline{x}}} \text{ or } -.67 = \frac{\overline{X} - 260}{3.75}$$

$$\overline{X} = \$260 - .67(3.75)$$
$$\overline{X} = \$260 - \$2.51$$
$$\overline{X} = \$257.49$$

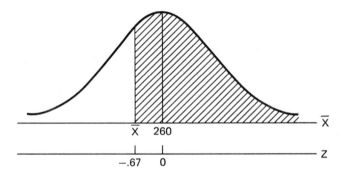

(g) Effect of the finite population correction factor on the standard error of the mean ($\sigma_x = \$15$, N=200, n=16).

Without correction factor: $\sigma_{\bar{x}} = \dfrac{\sigma_x}{\sqrt{n}} = \$3.75$

With correction factor: $\sigma_{\bar{x}} = \dfrac{\sigma_x}{\sqrt{n}} \sqrt{\dfrac{N-n}{N-1}}$

$$= \dfrac{15}{\sqrt{16}} \sqrt{\dfrac{200-16}{200-1}}$$

$$= \$3.75 \sqrt{.9246}$$

$$= \$3.75 \,(.9616)$$

$$= \$3.61$$

In this example, the finite population correction factor reduced the previously computed standard error of the mean by about 4%. When the sample comprises an appreciable portion of the population (n/N > .05), the finite population correction factor must be taken into account when computing the standard error of the mean.

Computation of $P(\$250 \leq \bar{X} \leq \$260)$ using $\sigma_{\bar{x}} = \dfrac{\sigma_x}{\sqrt{n}} \sqrt{\dfrac{N-n}{N-1}}$

$$Z = \frac{\overline{X} - \mu_x}{\frac{\sigma_x}{\sqrt{n}}\sqrt{\frac{N - n}{N - 1}}} = \frac{250 - 260}{3.61} = \frac{-10}{3.61}$$

$$= -2.77$$

$$P(\$250 \le \overline{X} \le \$260) = .4972$$

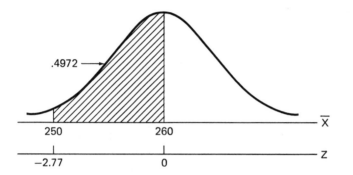

III. A securities analyst has determined that 65% of stockholders waive their rights to vote in the annual stockholders' meeting. If a random sample of 300 stockholders is selected, what is the probability that the sample proportion of stockholders waiving their voting rights will be:

(a) between .65 and .70?

(b) less than .58?

(c) Within what limits of the population percentage will 95% of the sample percentages fall?

SOLUTION

Sampling distribution of proportions is approximately normally distributed with mean = p = .65 and standard error of the proportion,

$$\sigma_{P_S} = \sqrt{\frac{p(1-p)}{n}} = \sqrt{\frac{(.65)(.35)}{300}} = .028$$

(a) $P(.65 \le p_S \le .70) = ?$

$$Z \cong \frac{p_S - p}{\sqrt{\frac{p(1-p)}{n}}} = \frac{.70 - .65}{.028} = \frac{.05}{.028} = 1.79$$

$P(.65 \le p_S \le .70) = .4633$

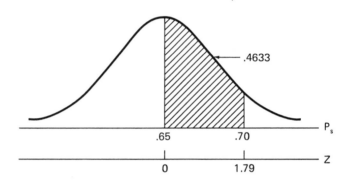

(b) $P(p_S < .58) = ?$

$$Z \cong \frac{.58 - .65}{.028} = \frac{-.07}{.028} = -2.50$$

$P(p_S < .58) = .5000 - .4938 = .0062$

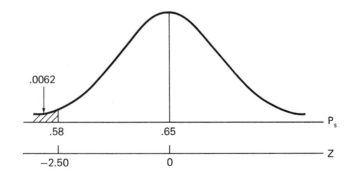

(c) Limits within which 95% of the sample percentages will fall:

$$-Z \cong \frac{\text{Ps}_L - p}{\sqrt{\dfrac{p(1 - p)}{n}}} \quad \text{and} \quad Z \cong \frac{\text{Ps}_U - p}{\sqrt{\dfrac{p(1 - p)}{n}}} \quad \text{Therefore,}$$

$$\text{Ps}_L = p - Z_L \sqrt{\frac{p(1 - p)}{n}} = .65 - (1.96)\,(.028) = .5951$$

$$\text{Ps}_U = p + Z_U \sqrt{\frac{p(1 - p)}{n}} = .65 + (1.96)\,(.028) = .7049$$

95% of all sample percentages will fall between 59.51% and 70.49%.

REVIEW PROBLEMS

I. The amount of time that a car mechanic spends replacing a muffler is normally distributed with a population mean of $\mu_x = 30$ minutes and standard deviation $\sigma_x = 5$ minutes.

(a) What proportion of mufflers will be replaced between 28 and 30 minutes?

(b) What proportion of mufflers will take more than 27 minutes to repair?

(c) If many random samples of 36 muffler replacements are selected:

1. What distribution would the same means follow?

2. What would the mean be expected to equal?

3. What would the standard error of the mean be expected to equal?

4. What proportion of the sample means would be between 28 and 30 minutes?

    5. What proportion of the sample means would be more than 27 minutes?

(d) Within what limits around the true mean would 99% of the sample means fall?

SOLUTION

(a) $Z = \dfrac{X - \mu_{\bar{x}}}{\sigma_x} = \dfrac{28 - 30}{5} = \dfrac{-2}{5} = -.40$

    $P(28 \le X \le 30) = .1554$

(b) $Z = \dfrac{27 - 30}{5} = \dfrac{-3}{5} = -.60$

    $P(X > 27) = .2257 + .5000 = .7257$

(c.1)   The sample means would follow a normal distribution.

(c.2)   The mean, $\mu_{\bar{x}} = \mu_x = 30$ minutes.

(c.3)   The standard error of the mean, $\sigma_{\bar{x}} = \dfrac{\sigma_x}{\sqrt{n}} = \dfrac{5}{\sqrt{36}} = .83$ minutes.

(c.4) $Z = \dfrac{\bar{X} - \mu_{\bar{x}}}{\dfrac{\sigma_x}{\sqrt{n}}} = \dfrac{28 - 30}{.83} = \dfrac{-2}{.83} = -2.41$

$$P(28 \leq \overline{X} \leq 30) = .4920$$

(c.5) $Z = \dfrac{27 - 30}{.83} = \dfrac{-3}{.83} = -3.61$

$$P(\overline{X} > 27) = .49985 + .5000 = .99985$$

(d) $-Z_L = \dfrac{\overline{X}_L - \mu_{\overline{x}}}{\sigma_{\overline{x}}}$ and $Z_U = \dfrac{\overline{X}_U - \mu_{\overline{x}}}{\sigma_{\overline{x}}}$

$\overline{X}_L = 30 - 2.58 \, (.83) = 27.86$ minutes

$\overline{X}_U = 30 + 2.58 \, (.83) = 32.14$ minutes

99% of the sample means will fall between 27.86 and 32.14 minutes.

II. The Book of the Month Club has determined that one-quarter of its members purchase the book offered as the monthly selection. If a random sample of 300 members is selected, what is the probability that:

(a) between .20 and .28 of the members will purchase this month's selection?

(b) less than .18 of the members will purchase this month's selection?

(c) Within what limits of the population proportion will 99% of the sample proportions fall?

SOLUTION

(a) $Z \cong \dfrac{p_s - p}{\sqrt{\dfrac{p(1-p)}{n}}} = \dfrac{.20 - .25}{\sqrt{\dfrac{.25\,(.75)}{300}}} = \dfrac{-.05}{.025} = -2.00$

$Z \cong \dfrac{.28 - .25}{.025} = \dfrac{.03}{.025} = 1.20$

$P(.20 \le p_s \le .28) = .4772 + .3849 = .8621$

(b) $Z \cong \dfrac{.18 - .25}{.025} = \dfrac{-.07}{.025} = -2.80$

$P(p_s < .18) = .5000 - .4974 = .0026$

(c) $P_{s_L} = p - Z_L \sqrt{\dfrac{p(1-p)}{n}} = .25 - 2.58\,(.025) = .1855$

$P_{s_U} = p + Z_U \sqrt{\dfrac{p(1-p)}{n}} = .25 + 2.58\,(.025) = .3145$

99% of the sample proportions will be between .1855 and .3145.

10

Estimation

In this chapter the concept of a sampling distribution is used to develop interval estimates of population parameters. The interval that is developed will vary depending on the value of the sample statistic. The level of confidence obtained refers to the probability that a sample correctly estimates the true value of the parameter in the population. The concept of a confidence interval is discussed for both quantitative data (means) and qualitative data (proportions). Moreover, the confidence interval estimation procedure is extended to determine the sample size necessary to achieve a desired level of confidence and sampling error. These procedures are also discussed for situations in which the samples are taken from finite populations.

MULTIPLE CHOICE

1. The type of reasoning involved in obtaining confidence interval estimates is called

   a. deductive reasoning.
   b. inductive reasoning.
   c. a posteriori reasoning.
   d. a priori reasoning.

2. Which of the following statements is false?

   a. There is a different critical value for each level of alpha.
   b. Alpha is the proportion in the tails of the distribution which are outside of the confidence interval.
   c. We can construct a 100% confidence interval estimate of μ_x.
   d. In practice the population mean is the unknown quantity that is to be estimated.

3. A 99% confidence interval estimate can be interpreted to mean that

   a. if all possible samples are taken, 99% of them would include the true population mean somewhere within their interval.
   b. we have 99% confidence that we have selected a sample whose interval does include the population mean.
   c. the means of 99% of the samples we could choose are accurate point estimates of the true population mean.
   d. a and b.

4. The value of $Z_{\alpha/2}$ chosen for constructing a confidence interval is called the

   a. sampling error.
   b. standard deviation.
   c. critical value.
   d. correction factor.

5. If you are constructing a 99% confidence interval of the population mean based on a sample of n=25 where the standard deviation of the sample is S=.05, the critical value of t will be

    a. 2.7969.
    b. 2.7874.
    c. 2.4922.
    d. 2.4851.

6. Which of the following is *not* true about the Student t distribution?

    a. It has more area in the tails and less in the center than does the normal distribution.
    b. It is used to construct confidence intervals for the population mean when the population standard deviation is known.
    c. It is bell-shaped and symmetric.
    d. As the number of degrees of freedom increases, the t distribution gradually approaches the normal distribution.

7. Suppose you want to determine the sample size needed for estimating the true proportion of customers who use a major credit card when purchasing merchandise. If you have no prior knowledge or estimate of the true proportion p, you should use

    a. $p = .25$
    b. $p = .50$
    c. $p = .75$
    d. $p = .99$

8. The manager of a typesetting service asks two employees to estimate the correct amount of duplicating fluid contained in two-gallon cans purchased from a local manufacturer. Both employees decide to construct a confidence interval for μ_x of the form $\overline{X} \pm 1.96 \dfrac{\sigma_x}{\sqrt{n}}$; but they disagree on the size of the samples to be drawn. Dan wants to sample 100 cans of duplicating fluid while Bob wants to sample 25 cans. How would their confidence intervals differ?

   a. Dan's interval would have a greater degree of confidence.
   b. Bob's interval would have a greater degree of confidence.
   c. Dan's interval would be narrower.
   d. Dan's interval would be wider.

EXAMPLES

I. A hardware store wants to estimate the correct length of wire wrapped on spools labeled as 45 feet. It is known from the manufacturer's specifications that the standard deviation of the length of wire on a spool is equal to .25 feet. A random sample of 25 spools is selected and the average length of wire wrapped on the spools is found to be 44.25 feet.

   (a) Set up a 95% confidence interval estimate of the true population average amount of wire wrapped around a spool.
   (b) Is the hardware store getting the length of wire that it assumes based on the labeling of this product?

SOLUTION

   (a) Confidence interval estimate for the mean (σ_x known and we assume the sample comes from a normal population):

$$\overline{X} \pm Z \frac{\sigma_x}{\sqrt{n}}$$

where

$$\overline{X} = 44.25 \text{ feet} \qquad n = 25$$
$$\sigma_x = .25 \text{ feet} \qquad Z = 1.96$$

$$44.25 \pm (1.96) \frac{.25}{\sqrt{25}} = 44.25 \pm 1.96 \,(.05)$$

$$= 44.25 \pm .098$$

$$44.152 \text{ feet} \le \mu_x \le 44.348 \text{ feet}$$

(b) No. Since 45 feet does not fall in the interval estimated to contain the true population mean, the hardware store is getting less wire than the spool indicates.

II. A company would like to estimate how much its employees pay in child-care costs per month in order to decide whether it would be worthwhile to provide a day-care center in its building. A random sample of 25 employees who use child care services revealed that on average they paid $360.52 in child-care costs with a standard deviation equal to $12.00.

(a) Set up a 95% confidence interval estimate of the true average of monthly child-care expenses.
(b) If only 400 employees have children requiring child-care services, find the 95% confidence interval estimate of the true average of monthly child-care expenses.

SOLUTION

(a) Confidence interval estimate for mean (σ_x unknown and we assume the sample comes from a normal population):

$$\overline{X} \pm t_{n-1} \frac{S}{\sqrt{n}}$$

where

$$\bar{X} = \$360.52 \qquad n = 25$$
$$S = \$12.00$$

$$360.52 \pm (2.0639) \frac{12}{\sqrt{25}} = 360.52 \pm (2.0639)\,(2.4)$$

$$= 360.52 \pm 4.95$$

$$\$355.57 \leq \mu_x \leq \$365.47$$

(b) Confidence interval estimate for the mean from a finite population (N=400). We use the finite population correction factor since $\frac{n}{N} > 5\%$.

$$\bar{X} \pm t_{n-1} \left(\frac{S}{\sqrt{n}}\right)\left(\sqrt{\frac{N-n}{N-1}}\right)$$

$$360.52 \pm (2.0639)\ \frac{12}{\sqrt{25}}\sqrt{\frac{400-25}{400-1}}$$

$$360.52 \pm (2.0639)\,(2.4)\,(\sqrt{.9398})$$

$$360.52 \pm (4.95)\,(.9695)$$

$$360.52 \pm 4.80$$

$$\$355.72 \leq \mu_x \leq \$365.32$$

III. The telephone company would like to estimate the proportion of customers who would be willing to pay for a modest increase in local phone calls if long distance charges were reduced significantly. A survey of 200 customers indicated that 80 customers would be willing to do this. Find the 95% confidence interval estimate of the true population proportion.

SOLUTION

Confidence interval estimate for the population proportion:

$$p_s \pm Z \sqrt{\frac{p_s\,(1 - p_s)}{n}}$$

$$p_s = \frac{X}{n} = \frac{80}{200} = .40 \qquad Z = 1.96$$

$$.40 \pm 1.96 \sqrt{\frac{(.40)\,(.60)}{200}} = .40 \pm 1.96 \sqrt{.0012}$$

$$= .40 \pm 1.96\,(.0346)$$

$$= .40 \pm .068$$

$$.332 \le p \le .468$$

IV. A large university wants to estimate the percentage of students who will attend commencement ceremonies. Last year's records show that 65% of the students attended commencement. What size sample is required to achieve a sample precision of ±5% with 90% confidence, if there are 5,000 students to be sampled from?

SOLUTION

Sample size determination for a proportion from a finite population ($N = 5{,}000$, $Z = 1.65$, $e = \pm .05$, and $p = .65$).

(1) Compute sample size without regard for correction factor.

$$n_0 = \frac{Z^2\,p(1 - p)}{e^2} = \frac{(1.65)^2\,(.65)\,(.35)}{(.05)^2}$$

$$= \frac{(2.7225)\,(.2275)}{.0025}$$

$$= \frac{.6194}{.0025} = 247.76$$

(2) Correct for finite population.

$$n = \frac{n_0 N}{n_0 + (N - 1)} = \frac{247.76 \ (5000)}{247.76 + (5000 - 1)}$$

$$= \frac{1238800}{5246.76}$$

$$= 237$$

V. A large university would like to estimate the average amount of money that alumni intend to donate this year. What size sample is needed if the university wants to have 95% confidence that its estimate is correct within ± $5? Based on records of donations from past years, the standard deviation is estimated to be $25.

SOLUTION

Sample size determination for the mean:

$$n = \frac{Z^2 \ \sigma_x^2}{e^2}$$

where

Z = critical value for confidence level desired = 1.96
e = sampling error permitted = ± $5
σ_x = standard deviation = $25

Therefore,

$$n = \frac{(1.96)^2 \ (25)^2}{5^2} = \frac{(3.8416) \ (625)}{25} = \frac{2401}{25} = 96.04 = 97$$

VI. A drug company is considering a request to pay for the continuing education of its 2500 research scientists. It would like to estimate the average amount of money spent by these scientists for professional memberships and one annual conference. What size sample is required to be 99% confident of being correct within ± $10? Based on a pilot study, the standard deviation, σ_x , is estimated to be $35.

SOLUTION

Sample size determination for means from a finite population ($N = 2500$, $Z = 2.58$, $e = \pm \$10$, and $\sigma_x = \$35$).

(1) Compute sample size without regard to correction factor.

$$n_0 = \frac{Z^2 \sigma_x^2}{e^2} = \frac{(2.58)^2 (35)^2}{(10)^2} = \frac{(6.6564) (1225)}{100}$$

$$= \frac{8154.09}{100}$$

$$= 81.5409$$

(2) Correct for finite population.

$$n = \frac{n_0 N}{n_0 + (N - 1)} = \frac{(81.5409) (2500)}{81.5409 + (2500 - 1)}$$

$$= \frac{203852.25}{2580.5409} = 78.996$$

$$= 79$$

REVIEW PROBLEMS

I. A Home Economics class at a university is interested in estimating the true amount of time that it takes to properly bake a well-known brand of cake mix. The directions given on the box indicate a baking time of 35 minutes, and it is known from the manufacturer's specifications that the standard deviation of the amount of time is 1.15 minutes. A random sample of 50 boxes of cake mix is selected and baked. The average amount of time taken to bake the cakes turned out to be 32.5 minutes.

(a) Set up a 90% confidence interval estimate of the true population average time required to bake this cake mix.
(b) Should the Home Economics class write to the manufacturer about the recommendation baking time for this product?

SOLUTION

Confidence interval estimate for the mean (σ_x known and we assume the sample comes from a normal population).

(a) $\overline{X} \pm Z \dfrac{\sigma_x}{\sqrt{n}}$

where

$$\overline{X} = 32.5 \qquad n = 50$$
$$\sigma_x = 1.15 \qquad Z = 1.65$$

$$32.5 \pm (1.65)\dfrac{1.15}{\sqrt{50}} = 32.5 \pm (1.65)\,(.1627)$$

$$= 32.5 \pm .27$$

$$32.23 \text{ minutes} \le \mu_x \le 32.77 \text{ minutes}$$

(b) Yes. Since 35 minutes does not fall in the interval estimated to contain the true population mean, the baking time recommended on the box is too long.

II. A large department store would like to estimate the amount of money that women spend per month on cosmetics. A survey is sent to a random sample of 90 female customers which indicates that women spend an average of $25.00 per month with a standard deviation of $3.50.

Find the 99% confidence interval estimate of the true average amount spent per month on cosmetics.

SOLUTION

Confidence interval estimate for mean (σ_x unknown and we assume the sample comes from a normal population).

$$\bar{X} \pm t_{n-1} \frac{S}{\sqrt{n}}$$

where

$$\bar{X} = \$25 \qquad\qquad n = 90$$
$$S = \$3.50$$

$$25 \pm (2.6322) \frac{3.5}{\sqrt{90}} = 25 \pm (2.6322)\,(.3689)$$

$$= 25 \pm .97$$

$$\$24.03 \le \mu_x \le \$25.97$$

III. A school district would like to determine the proportion of students who have access to a computer. The results of a survey sent to 300 randomly selected students shows that 175 of them have access to a computer. Construct a 90% confidence interval estimate for the true proportion of students who have access to a computer.

SOLUTION

Confidence interval estimate for the population proportion:

$$p_s \pm Z \sqrt{\frac{p_s (1 - p_s)}{n}}$$

$$p_s = \frac{X}{n} = \frac{175}{300} = .58 \qquad Z = 1.65$$

$$.58 \pm 1.65 \sqrt{\frac{(.58)(.42)}{300}} \qquad = .58 \pm 1.65 \sqrt{.0008}$$

$$= .58 \pm 1.65 (.028)$$

$$= .58 \pm .046$$

$$.534 \leq p \leq .626$$

IV. A company would like to estimate the proportion of employees who will attend the annual company picnic. The company's records show that half of the employees attended last year. How large a random sample should be taken to be within $\pm .05$ with 95% confidence, if there are 10,000 employees to be sampled from?

SOLUTION

Sample size determination for a proportion from a finite population (N = 10,000, Z = 1.96, e = ± .05, and p = .50).

(1) Compute sample size without regard for correction factor.

$$n_0 = \frac{Z^2 \, p(1-p)}{e^2} = \frac{(1.96)^2 \, (.5) \, (.5)}{(.05)^2}$$

$$= \frac{(3.84) \, (.25)}{.0025} = \frac{.96}{.0025}$$

$$= 384$$

(2) Correct for finite population.

$$n = \frac{n_0 \, N}{n_0 + (N-1)} = \frac{(384) \, (10,000)}{384 + (10,000 - 1)} = \frac{3,840,000}{10,383}$$

$$= 370$$

V. A community library is considering a proposal to purchase some video cassettes. A random sample of 400 out of 1,500 library members are selected and 275 indicate that they supported this proposal. Construct a 95% confidence interval estimate for the true proportion of library members who would support this proposal.

SOLUTION

Confidence interval estimate for the population proportion from a finite population
($N = 1,500$) using the finite population correction factor since $\frac{n}{N} > 5\%$.

$$p_s \pm Z \sqrt{\frac{p_s(1-p_s)}{n}} \; \sqrt{\frac{N-n}{N-1}}$$

$$p_s = \frac{275}{400} = .69 \qquad Z = 1.96$$

$$.69 \pm 1.96 \sqrt{\frac{(.69)(.31)}{400}} \; \sqrt{\frac{1,500 - 400}{1,500 - 1}}$$

$$.69 \pm 1.96\,(.0231)\,(.8566)$$

$$.69 \pm .039$$

$$.651 \le p \le .729$$

11

Hypothesis Testing I: Introduction and Concepts

In this chapter the concepts of sampling distributions and statistical inference are utilized to develop statistical hypothesis testing procedures. These methods enable decisions to be made concerning the value of a parameter (such as a mean or a proportion) based only on sample evidence. In making these decisions, two types of risk are involved. The Type I error α (the level of significance) represents the probability of erroneously concluding that the null hypothesis is false. The Type II error β represents the probability of not rejecting the null hypothesis when it is false. The concept of the power of a test $(1-\beta)$ is developed and the effect of varying the sample size, the level of significance, and the type of test on power is also considered.

MULTIPLE CHOICE

1. A statistician controls _____ by establishing the risk he or she is willing to tolerate in terms of rejecting a true null hypothesis.

    a. alpha
    b. beta
    c. gamma
    d. sigma

2. If a researcher rejects a true null hypothesis, she has

    a. made a correct decision.
    b. made a Type I error.
    c. made a Type II error.
    d. increased the power of the test.

3. If a 1% level of significance is used to test a null hypothesis, there is a probability of _____ of rejecting the null hypothesis when it is true.

    a. .005
    b. .010
    c. .995
    d. .990

4. The region of rejection for a one-tailed test is

    a. always less than .05.
    b. always smaller than that for any two-tailed test.
    c. found in the tail which supports the alternative hypothesis.
    d. found in the tail which supports the null hypothesis.

5. If a researcher specifies a 5% level of significance, then she will reject the null hypothesis only if her sample result differs from her hypothesized value by an amount that would occur by chance

    a. less than 5% of the time.
    b. more than 3% of the time.
    c. 95% of the time or more.
    d. 2.5% of the time or less.

6. Which of the following statements is false?

    a. H_0 refers to a specified value of the population parameter.
    b. The statement of H_0 always contains an equality.
    c. The statement of H_1 never contains an equality.
    d. H_0 refers to a specified value of the sample statistic.

7. The _____ measures how close the sample value has come to the null hypothesis.

    a. level of significance
    b. region of nonrejection
    c. test statistic
    d. critical value

8. When is it not possible to directly compare the results of a confidence interval estimate to the results obtained by testing a null hypothesis?

    a. if a two-tailed test of a hypothesis is used.
    b. if a one-tailed test of a hypothesis is used.
    c. if σ_x is unknown.
    d. a and c.

9. Which of the following can affect the power of a statistical test?

    a. the type of test (i.e., one-tailed or two-tailed).
    b. the level of significance chosen.
    c. sample size.
    d. All of the above.

EXAMPLES

I. A businessman is considering the purchase of a laundromat. The present owner claims that for the past five years an average day for the laundromat brought in $870 worth of business and that the standard deviation is equal to $50. The businessman agrees to buy the laundromat if there is evidence to support the present owner's claim. On 30 randomly selected days the businessman records the daily earnings of the laundromat and finds the mean equal to $855.

(a) Using the .05 level of significance, should the businessman conclude that the average earnings per day is different from $870?

(b) If the standard deviation was not known for the population, but the standard deviation for the sample S = $45, what would you conclude?

SOLUTION

Hypothesis test for mean of one sample (σ_x known).

(a) 1. H_0: $\mu_x = \$870$
   (i.e., the mean daily earnings is $870)

2. H_1: $\mu_x \neq \$870$
   (i.e., the mean daily earnings is not $870)

3. $\alpha = .05$

4. $n = 30$ days

5. Decision rule:

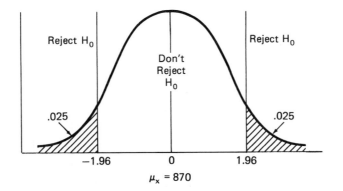

Reject H_0 if Z > + 1.96
          or if Z < − 1.96.
Otherwise, do not reject H_0.

6. Sample results:

$\overline{X} = \$855.00 \quad n = 30$

7. Test statistic:

$$Z = \frac{\overline{X} - \mu_x}{\frac{\sigma_x}{\sqrt{n}}} = \frac{855 - 870}{\frac{50}{\sqrt{30}}} = \frac{-15}{9.129} = -1.64$$

8. Conclusion:

Since $Z = -1.64$, we see that
$-1.96 \leq -1.64 \leq 1.96$.

Thus, our decision is not to reject H_0. There is no evidence that the average is different from \$870.

(b) Hypothesis test for mean σ_x unknown.

1. H_0: $\mu_x = \$870$

2. H_1: $\mu_x \neq \$870$

3. $\alpha = .05$

4. $n = 30$ days

5. Decision rule:

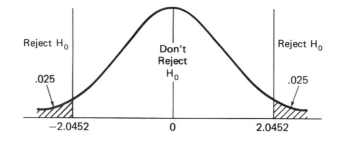

Reject if $t_{29} > 2.0452$
       or if $t_{29} < -2.0452$.
Otherwise, don't reject H_0.

6. Sample results:

$$\overline{X} = \$855, \qquad S = \$45, \qquad n = 30$$

7. Test statistic:

$$t_{n-1} = \frac{\overline{X} - \mu_x}{\dfrac{S}{\sqrt{n}}} = \frac{\$855 - 870}{\dfrac{45}{\sqrt{30}}} = \frac{-15}{8.22} = -1.82$$

8. Conclusion:

Since $t_{29} = -1.82$, we see that
$-1.82 \geq -2.0452$.

Thus, we do not reject H_0. At the .05 level of significance there is no evidence that the average is different from $870.

II. A dietician for the Health Department wants to determine if an 8 ounce carton of a particular brand of yogurt contains 120 mg of sodium as the labeling indicates. If she finds evidence that an 8 ounce serving contains more than 120 mg, she will no longer recommend this product to patients on a restricted diet. Using a random sample of 10 cartons, the dietician finds an average sodium content of 123.5 mg with a standard deviation equal to 3.5 mg. At the .05 level of significance, is there evidence that the average sodium content of an 8 ounce serving of this yogurt is more than 120 mg?

SOLUTION

Hypothesis test for mean of one sample (σ_x unknown).

1. $\mu_x \leq 120$ mg

2. $\mu_x > 120$ mg

3. $\alpha = .05$

4. n = 10 cartons

5. Decision rule:

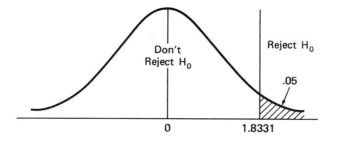

Reject H_0 if $t_9 > 1.8331$.
Otherwise, don't reject H_0.

6. Sample results:

$$\overline{X} = 123.5 \text{ mg}, \quad s = 3.5 \text{ mg}, \quad n = 10$$

7. Test statistic:

$$t_{n-1} = \frac{\overline{X} - \mu_x}{\frac{s}{\sqrt{n}}} = \frac{123.5 - 120.0}{\frac{3.5}{\sqrt{10}}} = \frac{3.5}{1.11} = 3.15$$

8. Conclusion:

Since $t_9 = 3.15$, we see that
$3.15 \geq 1.8331$.

Thus, we reject H_0 at the .05 level of significance. The average sodium content in one 8 ounce serving of this yogurt is greater than 120 mg.

III. An exterminator claims that his treatment lasts for 6 months, and that only 5% of his customers need a second treatment before 9 months have passed. In order to test this claim, a consumer group randomly selects 100 of the exterminator's customers and finds that 7 required a second treatment before 9 months had passed. Using the .01 level of significance, is the exterminator guilty of false advertising?

SOLUTION

Hypothesis test for proportion of one sample.

1. H_0: $p = .05$
   (i.e., the percent of customers needing a second treatment before 9 months pass).

2. H_1: $p \neq .05$
   (i.e., the percent of customers needing a second treatment before 9 months pass).

3. $\alpha = .01$

4. $n = 100$ customers

5. Decision rule:

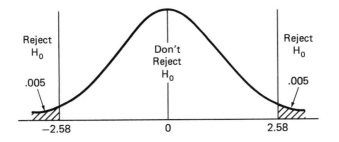

Reject H_0 if $Z > 2.58$
or if $Z < -2.58$.
Otherwise, do not reject H_0.

6. Sample results:

$$p_s = \frac{X}{n} = \frac{7}{100} = .07$$

7. Test statistic:

$$Z \cong \frac{p_s - p}{\sqrt{\dfrac{p(1-p)}{n}}} = \frac{.07 - .05}{\sqrt{\dfrac{(.05)(.95)}{100}}} = \frac{.02}{\sqrt{.000475}} = \frac{.02}{.022}$$

8. Conclusion:

Since $Z = .91$, we see that
$-2.58 < .91 < 2.58$

Thus, our decision is not to reject H_0. There is no evidence that the percentage of customers needing a second treatment before 9 months is different from 5%.

IV. The National Energy Commission requires the nuclear medicine departments of all hospitals to monitor the level of radioactive substances administered to patients. If the level of radioactive materials injected for a brain scan exceeds the recommended dosage of 150 Rads, the NEC requires an inspection of the hospital's materials and equipment. Past records on the dosage levels administered for brain scans show a standard deviation of 10 Rads. A random sample of 49 dosages is selected. The NEC is willing to take a 5% risk that a nuclear medicine department will be shut down for inspection when the level of radioactivity is 150 Rads or less.

(a) Compute the probability of shutting down a nuclear medicine department when the average level of radioactivity in a dosage is 151.0 Rads.
(b) Compute the probability of shutting down a nuclear medicine department when the average level of radioactivity in a dosage is 155 Rads.
(c) If the NEC wants to have a 90% chance of inspecting nuclear medicine departments when the average level of radioactivity in a dosage for a brain scan is 152.0 Rads, what sample size should be selected?

SOLUTION

This is an example of finding the power of the test $(1 - \beta)$—the probability of requiring an inspection for differing values of the true average level of radioactivity in a dosage for a brain scan.

1. H_0: $\mu_x \leq 150$ Rads
   (No inspection required.)

2. H_1: $\mu_x > 150$ Rads
   (Inspection required.)

3. $\alpha = .05$

4. $n = 49$, $\sigma_x = 10$ Rads

5. $\overline{X}_U = \mu_x + Z \dfrac{\sigma_x}{\sqrt{n}} = 150 + 1.645 \dfrac{10}{\sqrt{49}}$

$\overline{X}_U = 150 + 2.35$
    $= 152.35$

6. Decision rule:

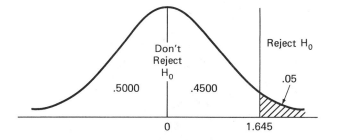

Reject H_0 if $\overline{X} > 152.35$.
Otherwise, do not reject H_0.

(a) Power $= 1 - \beta = P(\text{inspect when } \mu_1 = 151 \text{ Rads})$
               $= P(\overline{X} > 152.35 \text{ when } \mu_1 = 151 \text{ Rads}) = ?$

$$Z = \frac{\overline{X}_U - \mu_1}{\dfrac{\sigma_x}{\sqrt{n}}} = \frac{152.35 - 151.0}{\dfrac{10}{\sqrt{49}}} = \frac{1.35}{1.4286} = 0.94$$

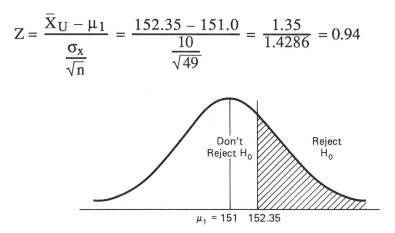

$$\text{Power} = P(\overline{X} > 152.35 \text{ when } \mu_1 = 151)$$
$$= P(\overline{X} > 152.35) = .5000 - .3264$$
$$= .1736$$

(b) $\text{Power} = 1 - \beta = P(\text{inspect when } \mu_1 = 155 \text{ Rads})$

$$= P(\overline{X} > 152.35 \text{ when } \mu_1 = 155 \text{ Rads}) = ?$$

$$Z = \frac{152.35 - 155}{\dfrac{10}{\sqrt{49}}} = \frac{-2.65}{1.4286} = -1.85$$

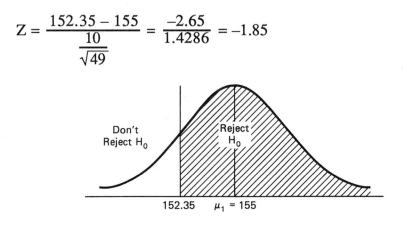

Power $= P(\overline{X} > 152.35 \text{ when } \mu_1 = 155)$
$$= .5000 + .4678$$
$$= .9678$$

(c) Sample size based on α and β risks.

$$n = \frac{\sigma_x^2 (Z_\alpha - Z_\beta)^2}{(\mu_0 - \mu_1)^2}$$

where

        σ_x^2 = the variance of the population = $(10)^2 = 100$

        Z_α = Z value for a given α level of significance (.05) = 1.645

        Z_β = Z value for a given β risk of Type II error (.10)
           = −1.28

μ_0 = value of the population mean under the null hypothesis

     = 150 Rads

μ_1 = value of the population mean under the alternative hypothesis

     = 152.0 Rads

$$n = \frac{(100)\,(1.645 - [-1.28])^2}{(150 - 152)^2}$$

$$= \frac{100\,(2.925)^2}{(-2)^2} = \frac{(100)\,(8.5556)}{4}$$

$$= \frac{855.56}{4} = 213.89 = 214$$

REVIEW PROBLEMS

I. A winery claims that the acidity level of its best wine has a pH = 6.00 and that no more than 11% of the bottles produced have an acidity level less than pH = 5.85. A random sample of 50 bottles is selected and the mean acidity level is pH = 5.92 with a standard deviation of .25. In addition, there were 6 bottles of wine with acidity levels less than pH = 5.85. (Use α = .01 in the following problems.)

  (a) Is there evidence to support the winery's claim that the acidity level of its best wine is pH = 6.00 valid?

  (b) Is there evidence to support the winery's claim that no more than 11% of the bottles produced have an acidity level less than pH = 5.85?

SOLUTION

(a) H_0: $\mu_x = 6.00$ (mean acidity level is pH = 6.00)
H_1: $\mu_x \neq 6.00$ (mean acidity level is not pH = 6.00)
$\alpha = .01$

Decision rule:

Reject H_0 if $t_{49} < -2.6800$
or if $t_{49} > 2.6800$
Otherwise, do not reject H_0.

Sample results:

$\bar{X} = 5.92$, $S = .25$, $n = 50$

Test statistic:

$$t_{49} = \frac{\bar{X} - \mu_x}{\frac{S}{\sqrt{n}}} = \frac{5.92 - 6.00}{\frac{.25}{\sqrt{50}}} = \frac{-.08}{.035}$$

$$= -2.29$$

Conclusion:

At the .01 level of significance do not reject H_0 since $-2.68 < -2.29 < 2.68$. There is no evidence that the winery's claim that the mean acidity is 6.00 is not valid.

(b) H_0: $p \leq .11$ (no more than 11% of the bottles have an acidity level less than pH = 5.85)
H_1: $p > .11$ (more than 11% of the bottles have an acidity level less than pH = 5.85)
$\alpha = .01$

Decision rule:

Reject H_0 if $Z > 2.33$
Otherwise, don't reject H_0.

Sample results:

$$p_s = \frac{X}{n} = \frac{6}{50} = .12$$

Test statistic:

$$Z = \frac{p_s - p}{\sqrt{\dfrac{p(1 - p)}{n}}} = \frac{.12 - .11}{\sqrt{\dfrac{(.11)(.89)}{50}}} = \frac{.01}{\sqrt{\dfrac{.0979}{50}}}$$

$$= \frac{.01}{\sqrt{.001958}} = \frac{.01}{.0442} = .226$$

Conclusion:

At the .01 level of significance do not reject H_0 since $Z = .226 < 2.33$. There is no evidence that more than 11% of the bottles have an acidity level less than $pH = 5.85$.

II. A manufacturer of salad dressings uses machines to dispense the liquid ingredients into bottles which move along an assembly line. The machine which dispenses ingredients for the French dressing is working properly when it dispenses 12 bottles of cider vinegar. The fluid ounces dispensed to each bottle is normally distributed with a standard deviation of .75 ounces. The production manager must stop the assembly line if there is evidence that the average amount of cider vinegar is more than 12 ounces. If a random sample of 25 bottles is selected, and the production manager is willing to have a risk of 5%, compute the power of the test and the probability of a Type II error (β) if the true population average amount of cider vinegar dispensed to a bottle is

(a) 12.75 ounces.
(b) 12.15 ounces.

(c) If the production manager wishes to have a 99% power of detecting a shift in the population mean from 12 ounces to 12.50 ounces, what sample size must be selected?

SOLUTION

This is an example of finding the power of the test $(1 - \beta)$—the probability of shutting the assembly line down for differing values of the true average of cider vinegar dispensed by a machine.

H_0: $\mu_x \leq 12$ ounces   (production process continues)
H_1: $\mu_x > 12$ ounces   (production process is halted)
$\alpha = .05$
$n = 25$, $\sigma_x = .75$ ounces
$\bar{X}_U = 12 + 1.645\left(\dfrac{.75}{\sqrt{25}}\right)$

$\quad\quad = 12 + (1.645)\,(.15)$
$\quad\quad = 12 + .25$
$\quad\quad = 12.25$

Decision rule:

Reject H_0 if $\overline{X} > 12.25$ ounces.
Otherwise, don't reject H_0.

(a) $Z = \dfrac{12.25 - 12.75}{\dfrac{.75}{\sqrt{25}}} = \dfrac{-.50}{.15} = -3.33$

P (Halt production when $\mu_1 = 12.75$) = $P(\overline{X} > 12.25$ when $\mu_1 = 12.75)$
= .5000 + .49957
= .99957

(b) $Z = \dfrac{12.25 - 12.15}{\dfrac{.75}{\sqrt{25}}} = \dfrac{.10}{.15} = .67$

P(Halt production when $\mu_1 = 12.15$) = $P(\overline{X} > 12.25$ when $\mu_1 = 12.15)$
= .5000 − .2486
= .2514

(c) $n = \dfrac{\sigma_x^2 (Z_\alpha - Z_\beta)^2}{(\mu_0 - \mu_1)^2} = \dfrac{(.75)^2 (1.645 - [-2.33])^2}{(12 - 12.50)^2}$

$= \dfrac{(.5625)\,(15.80)}{.25}$

$= \dfrac{8.888}{.25} = 36$

12

Hypothesis Testing II: Differences Between Quantitative Variables

In this chapter we shall extend our hypothesis testing concepts to additional procedures which are concerned with differences between quantitative variables. The difference between the means of two groups will be evaluated for both independent and related samples. Moreover, when the samples are independent, t-tests with and without the assumption of homogeneity of population variances are developed. In addition, the F-test for the equality of two population variances is considered.

MULTIPLE CHOICE

1. In order to use a t-test to determine whether there is a difference between the means of two independent populations, we assume that

    a. each population is normally distributed.
    b. the population variances are equal.
    c. the sample variances are equal.
    d. a and b.

2. In what type of test is the variable of interest the difference between the values of the observations rather than the observations themselves?

    (a.) test for the difference between means from two related populations
    b. test for the equality of variances from two independent populations
    c. test for the difference between the means of two independent populations
    d. a and c

3. Which of the following is **not** true about testing for the equality of variances from two independent populations?

    a. The statistical procedure is based upon the ratio of two sample variances.
    (b.) Only two-tailed tests can be used.
    c. The F distribution used for this statistical procedure depends upon two sets of degrees of freedom.
    d. If the data from each population are assumed to be normally distributed, then $\dfrac{s_1^2}{s_2^2}$ follows the F distribution.

4. A researcher wants to determine whether the variance for population #1 is greater than that for population #2 at the .05 level of significance. If the sample size is 16 for population #1 and 20 for population #2, what is (are) the critical value(s) on the F distribution?

    $t_{.95, 15}$ $t_{.95(20/15)}$

    (a.) 2.23
    b. 2.28 $t_{.95, 19}$
    c. 2.23 and .448
    d. 2.6 and .382

5. In testing for the equality of variances from two independent populations, one can use the

    a. normal distribution.
    b. t-distribution.
    (c.) F-distribution.
    d. a and b.

EXAMPLES

I. A furniture manufacturer is studying differences between four of its major outlets. The president of the company is particularly interested in the time it takes before customers receive furniture that has been ordered from the plant. Records of the delivery times for the most popular couch are shown for each of the four outlets below:

	--------------------------Outlet--------------------------			
	A	B	C	D
Sample size of Delivery Times Examined (n)	45	41	54	31
Average Delivery Time ($\overline{X}$)	40 days	34 days	37 days	43 days
Standard Deviation of Delivery Times (S)	2.6 days	2.0 days	2.5 days	3.0 days

For each of the problems below, use a .05 level of significance to determine:

(a) whether there is a difference in the mean times taken to deliver a couch for customers from Outlet A versus Outlet C.

(b) whether there is a difference in the variances in the times taken to deliver a couch for customers from Outlet B versus Outlet D.

SOLUTION

(a) Testing for the difference between the means of two populations— independent samples (assuming the population variances are equal).

    1. H_0: $\mu_A = \mu_C$ (There is no difference in the mean times taken to deliver a couch for customers from Outlet A versus Outlet C.)

2. H_1: $\mu_A \neq \mu_C$ (There is a difference in the mean times taken to deliver a couch for customers from Outlet A versus Outlet C.)

3. $\alpha = .05$

4. Decision rule:

> Reject H_0 if $t_{97} > 1.9847$
>   or if $t_{97} < -1.9847$
> Otherwise, don't reject H_0.
> (*Note:* df $= n_A + n_C - 2$
> $= 45 + 54 - 2$
> $= 97$)

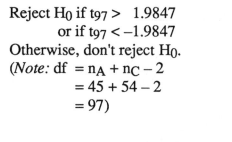

Reject H_0 Don't Reject H_0 Reject H_0

.025   .025

−1.9847   0   1.9847

5. Sample results:

A: $\bar{X}_A = 40$ days; $S_A = 2.6$ days; $n_A = 45$

C: $\bar{X}_C = 37$ days; $S_C = 2.5$ days; $n_C = 54$

6. Test statistic:

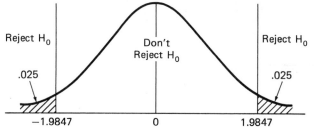

$$t_{n_A + n_B - 2} = \frac{\bar{X}_A - \bar{X}_C}{\sqrt{S_p^2 \left(\dfrac{1}{n_A} + \dfrac{1}{n_C}\right)}}$$

where

$$S_p^2 = \frac{(n_A - 1) \; S_A^2 + (n_C - 1) \; S_C^2}{n_A + n_C - 2}$$

$$= \frac{(45 - 1) \, (2.6)^2 + (54 - 1) \, (2.5)^2}{45 + 54 - 2}$$

$$= \frac{(44) \, (6.76) + (53) \, (6.25)}{97}$$

$$= \frac{297.44 + 331.25}{97} = \frac{628.69}{97} = 6.48$$

$$t_{97} = \frac{40 - 37}{\sqrt{(6.48) \left(\frac{1}{45} + \frac{1}{54}\right)}}$$

$$= \frac{3}{\sqrt{.2637}} = \frac{3}{.5135}$$

$$= 5.84$$

7. Conclusion:

Since $t_{97} = 5.84 > 1.9847$, reject H_0. The sample difference between Outlet A and Outlet C is much larger than what would have occurred by chance if the two populations had equal means. Thus, there is a significant difference in the average delivery time for a couch ordered from Outlet A versus Outlet C.

(b) Hypothesis test for the equality of variances from two populations (assume samples from normal populations).

1. H_0: $\sigma_B^2 = \sigma_D^2$

2. H_1: $\sigma_B^2 \neq \sigma_D^2$

3. $\alpha = .05$

4. Decision rule:

Reject H_0 if $F_{(40,30)} > 2.01$
or if $F_{(40,30)} < .515$
Otherwise, don't reject H_0.
(*Note:*

$$F_{L(a,b)} = \frac{1}{F_{U(b,a)}}$$

where a = number of degrees of freedom of group I = $n_I - 1$;
and b = number of degrees of freedom of group II = $n_{II} - 1$.)

$$F_{L(40,30)} = \frac{1}{F_{U(30,40)}} = \frac{1}{1.94} = .515$$

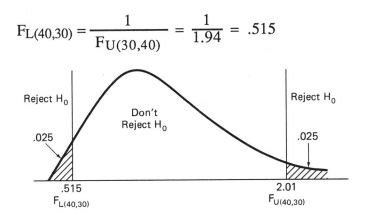

5. Sample results:

$S_B = 2.0$ days $S_D = 3.0$ days
$n_B = 41$ $n_D = 31$

6. Test statistic:

$$F_{(n_B-1), (n_D-1)} = F_{(40,30)} = \frac{S_B^2}{S_D^2} = \frac{2^2}{3^2} = \frac{4}{9} = .444$$

7. Conclusion:

Since $F_{(40,30)} = .444 < .515$, we reject H_0. There is evidence that there is a difference in the variances in the delivery times for Outlet B versus Outlet D.

II. A professor wants to determine whether two bookstores have significantly different prices for their books. From a list of the classics, the professor randomly chooses ten books and compares the prices of the two bookstores. The results of this study are shown below:

Book #	Bookstore A	Bookstore B
1	2.95	2.75
2	3.25	2.75
3	4.75	4.95
4	2.25	3.00
5	1.75	1.95
6	2.35	2.50
7	3.50	3.95
8	2.25	2.00
9	1.75	2.00
10	3.75	3.75

At the .05 level of significance, is there a significant difference between the prices at these two bookstores?

SOLUTION

1. H_0: $\mu_D = 0$ (There is no difference in the prices of books at the two different bookstores.)

2. H_1: $\mu_D \neq 0$ (There is a difference in the prices of books at the two different bookstores.)

3. $\alpha = .05$

4. Decision rule:

Reject H_0 if $t_9 > 2.2622$
or if $t_9 < -2.2622$
Otherwise, don't reject H_0.

5. Sample results:

Book #	Bookstore A	Bookstore B	$D_i = X_{A_i} - X_{B_i}$	D_i^2
1	2.95	2.75	.20	.0400
2	3.25	2.75	.50	.2500
3	4.75	4.95	−.20	.0400
4	2.25	3.00	−.75	.5625
5	1.75	1.95	−.20	.0400
6	2.35	2.50	−.15	.0225
7	3.50	3.95	−.45	.2025
8	2.25	2.00	.25	.0625
9	1.75	2.00	−.25	.0625
10	3.75	3.75	.00	.0000

$$\sum_{i=1}^{10} D_i = -1.05 \qquad \sum_{i=1}^{10} D_i^2 = 1.2825$$

$$\bar{D} = \frac{\sum_{i=1}^{n} D_i}{n} = \frac{-1.05}{10} = -.105$$

$$S_D = \sqrt{\frac{\displaystyle\sum_{i=1}^{n} D_i^2 - \frac{\left(\displaystyle\sum_{i=1}^{n} D_i\right)^2}{n}}{(n-1)}} = \sqrt{\frac{(1.2825) - \frac{(-1.05)^2}{10}}{9}}$$

$$= \sqrt{\frac{1.2825 - .11025}{9}}$$

$$= \sqrt{\frac{1.17225}{9}}$$

$$= \sqrt{.13025}$$

$$= .361$$

$$t_9 = \frac{\overline{D}}{\frac{S_D}{\sqrt{n}}} = \frac{-.105}{\frac{.361}{\sqrt{10}}} = \frac{-.105}{.114}$$

$$= -.92$$

Conclusion:

At the .05 level of significance we cannot reject H_0 since $t_9 = -.92$.
$-2.2622 < -.92 < 2.2622$

There is no evidence that there is a significant difference in the prices of books at these two bookstores.

REVIEW PROBLEMS

I. A chemical company has developed a new formula to kill roaches. In order to test whether this new formula is more effective than the original formula, a sample of 50 households was selected to test the products. Twenty-five households were randomly chosen to receive the original formula while the other 25 households were to receive the new formula. The number of days that each formula lasted was recorded by each household giving the following results:

New Formula	Old Formula
$\bar{X}_1 = 98$ days	$\bar{X}_2 = 90$ days
$S_1 = 4.5$ days	$S_2 = 4.0$ days

(a) Using the .01 level of significance, is there evidence of a difference in the variances between the new formula and the old formula?

(b) Using the .01 level of significance, is there evidence that the new formula is more effective than the old formula?

SOLUTION

(a) H_0: $\sigma_1^2 = \sigma_2^2$

H_1: $\sigma_1^2 \neq \sigma_2^2$

$\alpha = .01$

Decision rule:

> Reject H_0 if $F_{(24,24)} > 2.97$
> or if $F_{(24,24)} < .337$
> Otherwise, don't reject H_0.

$$F_{(24,24)} = \frac{S_1^2}{S_2^2} = \frac{(4.5)^2}{(4.0)^2} = \frac{20.25}{16.00} = 1.266$$

Conclusion:

> Since $F_{(24,24)} = 1.266$ falls in a region of non-rejection, we do not reject H_0. There is no evidence that the variance for the new formula is different from the variance of the old formula.

(b) H_0: $\mu_1 \leq \mu_2$ (i.e., $\mu_1 - \mu_2 \leq 0$)
H_1: $\mu_1 > \mu_2$ (i.e., $\mu_1 - \mu_2 > 0$)
$\alpha = .01$

Decision rule:

> Reject H_0 if $t_{48} > 2.4066$
> Otherwise, don't reject H_0.

Sample results:

> $\overline{X}_1 = 98$ days; $S_1 = 4.5$ days; $n_1 = 25$
> $\overline{X}_2 = 90$ days; $S_2 = 4.0$ days; $n_2 = 25$

$$S_p^2 = \frac{(n_1 - 1)\, S_1^2 + (n_2 - 1)\, S_2^2}{n_1 + n_2 - 2} = \frac{(24)\,(4.5)^2 + (24)\,(4.0)^2}{25 + 25 - 2}$$

$$= \frac{486 + 384}{48} = \frac{870}{48} = 18.125$$

$$t_{48} = \frac{\bar{X}_1 - \bar{X}_2}{\sqrt{S_p^2 \left(\dfrac{1}{n_1} + \dfrac{1}{n_2}\right)}}$$

$$= \frac{98 - 90}{\sqrt{18.125 \left(\dfrac{1}{25} + \dfrac{1}{25}\right)}}$$

$$= \frac{8}{\sqrt{18.125\,(.08)}}$$

$$= \frac{8}{\sqrt{1.45}} = 6.64$$

Conclusion:

Since $t_{48} = 6.64 > 2.4066$, we would reject H_0. There is evidence that the new formula is more effective than the old formula.

II. A health club would like to show that one of its new programs helps members lose weight. A random sample of 9 participants in this program was asked to record their weight before and after this program. The results are shown below:

Participant	Before	After	DI	D_i^2
1	135	115	20	400
2	171	165	6	36
3	142	130	12	144
4	119	115	4	16
5	121	126	5	25
6	165	155	10	100
7	172	168	4	16
8	193	183	10	100
9	203	195	8	64

$$\Sigma = \frac{79}{9} \quad \bar{D} = 8.778$$

$$\Sigma D_i^2 = 99$$

Is there a significant reduction in the average weight after participating in this program? (Use $\alpha = .01$.)

SOLUTION

The paired t-test for related samples (assume samples come from normal populations).

H_0: $\mu_D \le 0$
H_1: $\mu_D > 0$
$\alpha = .01$

Decision rule:

Reject H_0 if $t_8 > 2.8965$
Otherwise, don't reject H_0.

Participant #	Before	After	$D_i = X_{B_i} - X_{A_i}$	D_i^2
1	135	115	20	400
2	171	165	6	36
3	142	130	12	144
4	119	115	4	16
5	121	126	−5	25
6	165	155	10	100
7	172	168	4	16
8	193	183	10	100
9	203	195	8	64

$$\sum_{i=1}^{9} D_i = 69 \qquad \sum_{i=1}^{9} D_i^2 = 901$$

$$\bar{D} = \frac{\Sigma D_i}{n} = \frac{69}{9} = 7.67$$

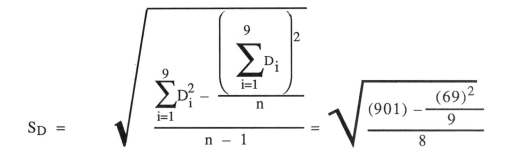

$$S_D = \sqrt{\frac{\sum_{i=1}^{9} D_i^2 - \frac{\left(\sum_{i=1}^{9} D_i\right)^2}{n}}{n-1}} = \sqrt{\frac{(901) - \frac{(69)^2}{9}}{8}}$$

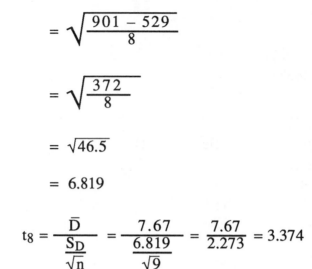

$$= \sqrt{\frac{901 - 529}{8}}$$

$$= \sqrt{\frac{372}{8}}$$

$$= \sqrt{46.5}$$

$$= 6.819$$

$$t_8 = \frac{\bar{D}}{\frac{S_D}{\sqrt{n}}} = \frac{7.67}{\frac{6.819}{\sqrt{9}}} = \frac{7.67}{2.273} = 3.374$$

Conclusion:

Since $t_8 = 3.374 > 2.8965$, reject H_0. There is evidence that there is a weight loss after participating in this program.

13

Hypothesis Testing III: Differences Between Proportions and Other Chi-Square Tests

This chapter focuses primarily on tests for proportions and various chi-square methods. For qualitative data and independent samples, a test for the difference between two proportions is developed using two methods—the normal approximation and the chi-square technique. In addition, when dealing with related samples the McNemar test for the difference between two proportions is described. Moreover, in this chapter, several tests based on chi-square are discussed. The chi-square test is extended to the case of more than two groups and generalized as a test of independence between two qualitative variables. Furthermore, the chi-square test is also utilized to determine the goodness of fit of a set of data to a specific probability distribution. Finally, the one-sample (chi-square) test for the variance in the population is considered.

MULTIPLE CHOICE

1. In the chi-square method of analysis, the squared difference between the observed frequency, f_O, and the theoretical frequency, f_T, is computed. If there is no real difference in the population proportion, then this squared difference should be:

    a. one.
    b. small.
    c. large.
    d. cannot be determined.

2. When using the chi-square method of analysis to test for the difference between two proportions, the degrees of freedom are equal to

    a. $n-1$
    b. $n_1 + n_2 - 2$
    c. $(r-1)(c-1)$
    d. $(r-1) + (c-1)$

3. Which of the following is *not* true about the chi-square distribution?

    a. It is a skewed distribution.
    b. Its shape depends solely on the number of degrees of freedom.
    c. As the number of degrees of freedom increases, the chi-square distribution becomes more symmetrical.
    d. All of the above are true.

4. If we use the chi-square method of analysis to test for the difference between proportions, we must assume that there are at least _____ theoretical frequencies in each cell of the contingency table.

    a. 5
    b. 30
    c. 50
    d. 100

5. If a chi-square test indicates that there is no difference between two proportions, this means that

   a. there is a relationship between the variables.
   b. two variables are independent.
   c. two variables are dependent.
   d. a and c

6. The interrelationship between the normal distribution and the chi-square distribution with one degree of freedom shows us that

   a. the chi-square statistic will always be the square of the test statistic based upon the normal distribution.
   b. the critical value of the chi-square distribution is the square of the critical value of the normal distribution.
   c. the normal distribution and chi-square tests will lead to the same conclusion.
   d. All of the above.

7. For which of the following is the chi-square distribution inappropriate?

   a. a one-tailed test for the difference of proportions
   b. a two-tailed test for the difference of proportions
   c. a test for the goodness of fit of a set of data to a specific probability distribution
   d. a test of a hypothesis about a population variance

EXAMPLES

I. The owner of a car dealership conducted a survey to determine whether there was a gender difference in one's satisfaction with the service received. A sample of 100 women showed that 65 were satisfied, while a sample of 110 men showed that 80 were satisfied. At the .01 level of significance, is there evidence of a difference in the satisfaction of men versus women?

   (a) Solve this problem using the normal distribution.
   (b) Solve this problem using the chi-square distribution.

SOLUTION

(a) Hypothesis test for difference between proportions from two independent populations using the normal distribution test.

1. H_0: $p_m = p_w$

2. H_1: $p_m \neq p_w$

3. $\alpha = .01$

4. $n_m = 110$; $n_w = 100$

5. Decision rule:

> Reject H_0 if $Z >$ 2.58
> or if $Z < -2.58$
> Otherwise, don't reject H_0.

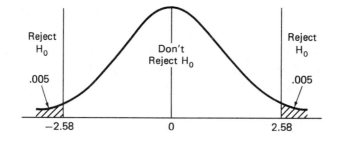

6. Sample results:

$$p_{s_m} = \text{sample proportion of satisfied men} = \frac{X_m}{n_m} = \frac{80}{110} = .727$$

$$p_{s_w} = \text{sample proportion of satisfied women} = \frac{X_w}{n_w} = \frac{65}{100} = .65$$

$$\bar{p} = \text{pooled estimate of the population proportion} = \frac{X_m + X_w}{n_m + n_w}$$

$$= \frac{80 + 65}{110 + 100} = \frac{145}{210} = .69$$

7. Test statistic:

$$Z \cong \frac{(p_{s_1} - p_{s_2})}{\sqrt{\bar{p}(1 - \bar{p}) \left(\frac{1}{n_1} + \frac{1}{n_2}\right)}}$$

$$= \frac{(.727 - .650)}{\sqrt{(.69)(1 - .69) \left(\frac{1}{110} + \frac{1}{100}\right)}}$$

$$= \frac{.077}{\sqrt{(.69)(.31)(.009 + .010)}}$$

$$= \frac{.077}{\sqrt{(.2139)(.019)}}$$

$$= \frac{.077}{\sqrt{.00406}} = \frac{.077}{.0637} = 1.21$$

8. Conclusion:

Since $Z = 1.21$, we see that $-2.58 < 1.21 < 2.58$, and we do not reject H_0. There is no evidence that men and women differ in their satisfaction with the service received at the dealership.

(b) Chi-square test for the difference between two proportions.

1. H_0: $p_m = p_w$ (There is no difference between the proportion of men who are satisfied and the proportion of women who are satisfied.)

2. H_1: $p_m \neq p_w$ (There is a difference between the proportion of men who are satisfied and the proportion of women who are satisfied.)

3. $\alpha = .01$

4. Decision rule:

Reject H_0 if $\chi_1^2 > 6.635$

Otherwise, don't reject H_0.

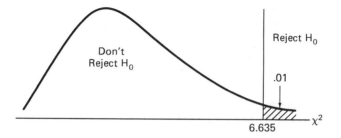

5. Sample results:

Satisfied	Men	Women	Totals
Yes	80 (75.95)	65 (69.05)	145
No	30 (34.05)	35 (30.95)	65
Totals	110	100	210

( ) Bracketed numbers are theoretical frequencies.

6. Test statistic:

$$\chi^2_{(r-1)(c-1)} \cong \sum_{\text{all cells}} \frac{(f_o - f_T)^2}{f_T}$$

where
f_o = observed frequency in each cell
f_T = theoretical frequency in each cell = $\frac{n_r n_c}{n}$

where

$$n_r \; = \text{total number in row}$$
$$n_c \; = \text{total number in column}$$
$$n \; \; = \text{total sample size}$$

$$r \; = \text{number of rows in the contingency table}$$
$$c \; = \text{number of columns in the contingency table}$$

$(r{-}1)\,(c{-}1) = \text{number of degrees of freedom.}$
(*Note:* The degrees of freedom for a test of c proportions is actually c–1.)

$$f_T = \frac{(145)\,(110)}{210} = 75.95 \qquad\qquad f_T = \frac{(145)\,(100)}{210} = 69.05$$

$$f_T = \frac{(65)\,(110)}{210} = 34.05 \qquad\qquad f_T = \frac{(65)\,(100)}{210} = 30.95$$

f_o	f_T	$(f_o - f_T)$	$(f_o - f_T)^2$	$\dfrac{(f_o - f_T)^2}{f_T}$
80	75.95	4.05	16.4025	.21596
30	34.05	–4.05	16.4025	.48172
65	69.05	–4.05	16.4025	.23755
35	30.95	4.05	16.4025	.52997

$$\chi_1^2 = 1.46520$$

7. Conclusion:

Since $\chi_1^2 = 1.46520 < 6.635$, do not reject H_0.

There is no evidence of a significant difference between the proportions of men and women who were satisfied with the service received at this dealership.

Note: $\chi_1^2 = 1.46520 \cong (Z = 1.21)^2$

and $\chi_1^2 = 6.635 \cong (Z = 2.576)^2$

II. The manager of a Move-It-Yourself rental service recorded the number of trucks rented per day for 90 days. The results are presented in the table below.

Number of Trucks Rented	Frequency
0	5
1	9
2	12
3	17
4	18
5	15
6	14
	90

Does the distribution of the number of trucks rented per day in the 90-day period follow a Poisson distribution at the .01 level of significance?

SOLUTION

Chi-square goodness of fit test for a Poisson distribution.

1. H_0: The number of trucks rented per day follows a Poisson distribution.

2. H_1: The number of trucks rented per day follows a probability distribution other than a Poisson distribution.

3. $\alpha = .01$

4. Decision rule:

Reject H_0 if $\chi_5^2 > 15.086$

Otherwise, don't reject H_0.

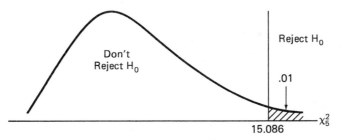

5. Sample results:

Number of Trucks Rented Per Day (X_j)	Number of Days (f_j)	X_jf_j	Poisson Probability $P(X_j \text{ given } \mu_x = 3.5)$	Theoretical Frequency $f_T = nP(X_j)$
0	5	0	.0302	2.718
1	9	9	.1057	9.513
2	12	24	.1850	16.650
3	17	51	.2158	19.422
4	18	72	.1888	16.992
5	15	75	.1322	11.898
6	14	84	.0771	6.939
7 or more	0	0	.0652	5.868
Totals	90	315	1.0000	90.000

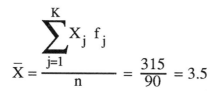

$$\bar{X} = \frac{\sum_{j=1}^{K} X_j\, f_j}{n} = \frac{315}{90} = 3.5$$

6. Test statistic:

$$\chi^2_{K-p-1} \simeq \sum_{\text{all cells}} \frac{(f_0 - f_t)^2}{f_T}$$

where

f_0	=	the observed frequency
f_T	=	the theoretical frequency
K	=	the number of categories or classes that remain after collapsing classes = 7
p	=	the number of parameters estimated from the data = 1 (i.e., estimate of mean of Poisson distribution)
$K - p - 1$	=	the degrees of freedom = 5

Number of Trucks Rented Per Day	f_0	f_T	$(f_0 - f_T)$	$(f_0 - f_T)^2$	$\dfrac{(f_0 - f_T)^2}{f_T}$
1 or fewer	14	12.231	1.769	3.129	0.2558
2	12	16.650	−4.650	21.623	1.2987
3	17	19.422	−2.422	5.866	0.3020
4	18	16.992	1.008	1.016	0.0598
5	15	11.898	3.102	9.622	0.8087
6	14	6.939	7.061	49.858	7.1852
7 or more	0	5.868	−5.868	34.433	5.8679

$$\chi^2_5 = 15.7781$$

7. Conclusion:

Since $\chi_5^2 = 15.7781 > 15.086$, we reject H_0.

The manager of the Move-It-Yourself rental service can conclude that the distribution of the number of trucks rented per day does not follow a Poisson distribution.

III. Suppose a banker wants to determine whether the proportion of customers who indicated that they intended to open up an IRA in the next year differed from the actual proportion of customers who opened an IRA during that year. A random sample of 600 customers was selected; they indicated their intentions toward investing in an IRA and whether, in fact, they made that investment during the following year. The results were as follows:

Intention to Invest in an IRA	Investment Made in an IRA During the Following Year		
	Yes	No	Totals
Yes	325	71	396
No	12	192	204
Totals	337	263	600

At the .05 level of significance, is there a difference in the proportion of customers who intended to invest in an IRA and the actual proportion of customers who did make this investment?

SOLUTION

The McNemar test for difference between proportions from two related populations.

1. H_0: $p_1 = p_2$

2. H_1: $p_1 \neq p_2$

3. $\alpha = .05$

4. Decision rule:

Reject H_0 if $Z > 1.96$
or if $Z < -1.96$
Otherwise, don't reject H_0.

5. For our data:

$$A = 325$$
$$B = 71$$
$$C = 12$$
$$D = 192$$

and the sample proportion of customers intending to invest in an IRA (p_{s_1}) and customers who actually invested (p_{s_2}) are:

$$p_{s_1} = \frac{A + B}{n} = \frac{325 + 71}{600} = \frac{396}{600} = .66$$

$$p_{s_2} = \frac{A + C}{n} = \frac{325 + 12}{600} = \frac{337}{600} = .56$$

6. Test statistic:

$$Z = \frac{B - C}{\sqrt{B + C}} = \frac{71 - 12}{\sqrt{71 + 12}} = \frac{59}{\sqrt{83}} = \frac{59}{9.11} = 6.48$$

7. Conclusion:

Since $Z = 6.48 > 1.96$, we reject H_0. There is evidence that the proportion of customers who intended to invest in an IRA is different from the proportion of customers who actually did make this investment.

IV. Suppose that the population standard deviation for the daily mileage recorded for a New York taxicab service is 25 miles. If a random sample of 50 taxis showed a sample standard deviation of 20 miles, is there evidence at the .05 level of significance that the population standard deviation has changed?

SOLUTION

Hypothesis test for a population variance (assume that the sample is from a normal population).

    1. H_0: $\sigma_x = 25$ miles (or $\sigma_x^2 = 625$)

    2. H_1: $\sigma_x \neq 25$ miles (or $\sigma_x^2 \neq 625$)

    3. $\alpha = .05$

    4. Decision rule:

        Reject H_0 if $\chi_{49}^2 > 70.222$

        or if $\chi_{49}^2 < 31.555$

        Otherwise, don't reject H_0.
        (*Note:* df = n–1 = 50–1 = 49)

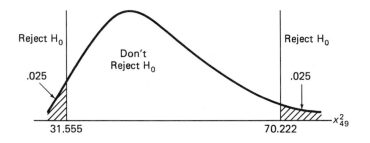

    5. Sample results:

        S = 20 miles; n = 50

6. Test statistic:

$$\chi_{49}^2 = \frac{(n-1)S^2}{\sigma_x^2} = \frac{(50-1)\,(20)^2}{(25)^2} = \frac{(49)\,(400)}{625} = \frac{19600}{625} = 31.36$$

7. Conclusion:

Reject H_0 since $\chi_{49}^2 = 31.36 > 31.555$.

There is evidence that the population standard deviation has changed from 25 miles at the .05 level of significance.

REVIEW PROBLEMS

I. An advertising agency wanted to determine whether there was a relationship between place of residence and reaction to a new commercial. A random sample of 175 people from suburbs, 150 people from rural areas, and 200 people from large cities was selected. After viewing the commercial each viewer was asked if he or she liked the commercial. The results are presented in the table below:

Reaction to Commercial	--------------------Place of Residence--------------------			
	Suburb	Rural Area	Large City	Totals
Positive	105 108.3	45 92.86	175 123.8	325
Negative	70	105	25 76.19	200
Totals	175 66.667	150 57.14	200	525

At the .05 level of significance, is there any evidence of a difference in the reaction to this commercial by place of residence?

SOLUTION

Testing for the difference between proportions from 3 independent populations.

     1. H_0: $p_1 = p_2 = p_3$

     2. H_1: At least one proportion is different from the others.

     3. $\alpha = .05$

     4. Decision rule:

         Reject H_0 if $\chi_2^2 > 5.991$

         Otherwise, don't reject H_0.

5. Sample results:

Reaction to Commercial	Place of Residence			Totals
	Suburb	Rural Area	Large City	
Positive	105 (108.33)	45 (92.86)	175 (123.81)	325
Negative	70 (66.67)	105 (57.14)	25 (76.19)	200
Totals	175	150	200	525

( ) Bracketed numbers are theoretical frequencies.

6. Test statistic:

$$\chi_2^2 \cong \sum_{\text{all cells}} \frac{(f_o - f_T)^2}{f_T}$$

f_o	f_T	$(f_o - f_T)$	$(f_o - f_T)^2$	$\dfrac{(f_o - f_T)^2}{f_T}$
105	108.33	−3.33	11.09	.1024
70	66.67	3.33	11.09	.1663
45	92.86	−47.86	2290.58	24.6670
105	57.14	47.86	2290.58	40.0872
175	123.81	51.19	2620.42	21.1648
25	76.19	−51.19	2620.42	34.3932

$$\chi_2^2 = 120.5809$$

7. Conclusion:

Since $\chi_2^2 = 120.5809 > 5.991$, reject H_0.

There is evidence that at least one proportion is different from the others. That is, there is a relationship between place of residence and reaction to the commercial.

II. A manufacturer of candy must monitor the temperature of its candies throughout the cooking process. The mean temperature required for its special fudge is 238°F. Records show that the standard deviation for this process is 1°F. A random sample of 30 batches of fudge is selected and the temperature at which these are cooked is measured. The sample standard deviation is 2°F. At the .01 level of significance, is there evidence that the population standard deviation has changed?

SOLUTION

Hypothesis test for a population variance (assume that the sample is from a normal population).

H_0: $\sigma_x = 1$ (or $\sigma_x^2 = 1$)

H_1: $\sigma_x \neq 1$ (or $\sigma_x^2 \neq 1$)

$\alpha = .01$

Decision rule:

Reject H_0 if $\chi_{29}^2 > 52.336$

or if $\chi_{29}^2 < 13.121$

Otherwise, don't reject H_0.
(*Note:* df = n − 1 = 30 − 1 = 29)

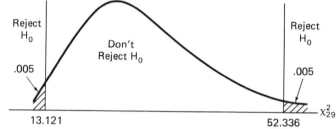

Sample results:

S = 2;   n = 30

Test statistic:

$$\chi_{29}^2 = \frac{(n-1)\ S^2}{\sigma_x^2} = \frac{(30-1)\ (2)^2}{1^2} = \frac{(29)\ (4)}{1} = \frac{116}{1} = 116$$

Conclusion:

Reject H_0, since $\chi_{29}^2 = 116 > 52.336$.

There is evidence that the population standard deviation has changed.

14

The Analysis of Variance

When dealing with quantitative data, a problem of frequent interest to the researcher is the comparison of several groups. For example, an auditor for the Internal Revenue Service might want to compare the processing speed at several regional offices. In this chapter, then, we are concerned with methods for testing for possible differences between the means of several groups. The methodology considered is classified under the general title of the "analysis of variance." One-factor, randomized block, and two-factor models are described.

MULTIPLE CHOICE

1. The analysis of variance methodology will show that there really is a difference between the means of several groups when

  a. the variance within groups is significantly larger than the variance between groups.
  b. the variance between groups is significantly larger than the variance within groups.
  c. the sum of squares within groups equals the total sum of squares.
  d. a and b.

2. The shape of the F distribution depends upon

  a. the mean and the standard deviation.
  b. the sizes of the samples.
  c. the degrees of freedom between group means and the degrees of freedom within groups.
  d. the number of groups in the analysis.

3. The variance between groups is equal to

  a. $\dfrac{SSB}{c-1}$

  b. $\sum\limits_{j=1}^{c} n_j\,(\bar{X}_j - \bar{\bar{X}})^2$

  c. $\dfrac{SSB}{n-c}$

  d. $SST - SSW$

4. Which of the following is used to test the assumption of homogeneity of variance?

  a. Fisher's F test
  b. Hartley's test
  c. Tukey's T method
  d. Student's t test

5. Which of the following comparisons is made in the Tukey T method?

    a. The variance between groups is compared to the variance within groups.

    b. The sum of squares between groups is compared to the total sum of squares.

    c. The means of each group are compared to the grand mean.

    d. The differences $(\bar{X}_j - \bar{X}_{j'})$ among all $\dfrac{c\,(c-1)}{2}$ pairs of means are compared to a critical range.

EXAMPLES

I. New York City's Health Department wanted to compare the length of effectiveness (in days) of three brands of roach killer to determine if one provided longer protection than the others. A random sample of five packages of each brand was tested with the following results: $n = 5$

Brand 1	Brand 2	Brand 3	
75	92	89	256
79	89	90	258
77	93	87	257
82	94	90	266
80	88	88	256
$\Sigma = 393$	$\Sigma = 456$	$\Sigma = 444$	$1293 = G \cdot T$

(a) At the .05 level of significance, is there evidence of a difference in the variances of the three brands of roach killers?

(b) At the .05 level of significance, is there evidence of a difference in the average length of effectiveness (in days) for the three brands of roach killer?

(c) At the .05 level of significance, determine which of the three brands of roach killer are significantly different from each other.

SOLUTION

(a) H_0: $\sigma_1^2 = \sigma_2^2 = \sigma_3^2$
H_1: Not all σ_j^2 are equal (j = 1,2,3)
$\alpha = .05$

Decision rule:

Reject H_0 if $F_{MAX\ (3,4)} > 15.5$
Otherwise, don't reject H_0.

	Brand 1	Brand 2	Brand 3	
	75	92	89	
	79	89	90	
	77	93	87	
	82	94	90	
	80	88	88	
T_j:	393	456	444	$GT = \sum\limits_{j=1}^{3} T_j = 1293$
n_j:	5	5	5	$n = \sum\limits_{j=1}^{3} n_j = 15$
$\bar{X}_j$:	78.6	91.2	88.8	$(GT)^2 = 1{,}671{,}849$
T_j^2:	154,449	207,936	197,136	$\dfrac{(GT)^2}{n} = \dfrac{1{,}671{,}849}{15}$
				$= 111{,}456.6$

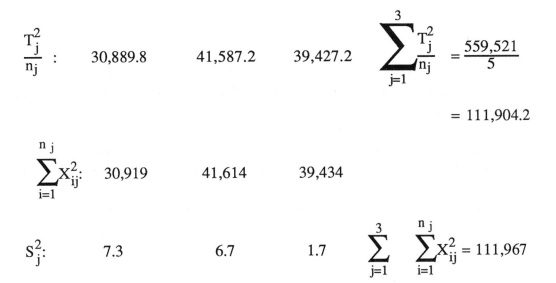

$$\frac{T_j^2}{n_j} : \qquad 30{,}889.8 \qquad 41{,}587.2 \qquad 39{,}427.2 \qquad \sum_{j=1}^{3} \frac{T_j^2}{n_j} = \frac{559{,}521}{5}$$

$$= 111{,}904.2$$

$$\sum_{i=1}^{n\ j} X_{ij}^2 : \quad 30{,}919 \qquad 41{,}614 \qquad 39{,}434$$

$$S_j^2 : \qquad 7.3 \qquad\qquad 6.7 \qquad\qquad 1.7 \qquad \sum_{j=1}^{3}\ \sum_{i=1}^{n\ j} X_{ij}^2 = 111{,}967$$

Test statistic and sample results:

$$F_{MAX\,(c,(\bar{n}-1))} = \frac{S_{MAX}^2}{S_{MIN}^2}$$

where
$$c = \text{number of groups} = 3$$

$$\bar{n} = \frac{\displaystyle\sum_{j=1}^{c} n_j}{c} = \frac{n}{c} = \frac{15}{3} = 5 \qquad \text{(only integer portion of value is used in obtaining degrees of freedom)}$$

$$S_{MAX}^2 = \text{largest sample variance} = 7.3$$

$$S_{MIN}^2 = \text{smallest sample variance} = 1.7$$

$$F_{MAX(3,4)} = \frac{7.3}{1.7} = 4.29$$

Conclusion:

Since $F_{MAX(3,4)} = 4.29 < 15.5$, we do not reject H_0. There is no evidence of a difference in the variances of the three brands of roach killer.

(b) H_0: $\mu_1 = \mu_2 = \mu_3$ (i.e., there are no differences in the mean length of protection provided by the 3 brands of roach killer)

H_1:   There is a difference in the mean length of protection provided by at least one pair of brands.

$\alpha = .05$

Decision rule:

Reject H_0 if $F_{(2,12)} > 3.89$
Otherwise, do not reject H_0.

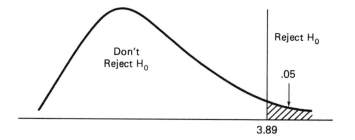

Sample results and test statistic:

$$SSB = \sum_{j=1}^{c} \frac{T_j^2}{n_j} - \frac{(GT)^2}{n} = 111{,}904.2 - 111{,}456.6 = 447.6$$

$$SSW = \sum_{j=1}^{c} \sum_{i=1}^{n_j} X_{ij}^2 - \sum_{j=1}^{c} \frac{T_j^2}{n_j} = 111{,}967 - 111{,}904.2 = 62.8$$

$$SST = \sum_{j=1}^{c} \sum_{i=1}^{n_j} X_{ij}^2 - \frac{(GT)^2}{n} = 111{,}967 - 111{,}456.6 = 510.4$$

ANALYSIS OF VARIANCE TABLE

Source	Sum of Squares	Degrees of Freedom	Mean Square Variance	F
Between Brands	447.6	$c - 1 =$ $3 - 1 = 2$	$MSB = \dfrac{447.6}{2}$ $= 223.8$	$F = \dfrac{223.8}{5.23}$ $= 42.79$
Within Brands	62.8	$n - c =$ $15 - 3 = 12$	$MSW = \dfrac{62.8}{12}$ $= 5.23$	
Total	510.4	$n - 1 =$ $15 - 1 = 14$		

Conclusion:

Reject H_0 since $42.79 > 3.89$. There is a significant difference between at least one pair of the brands in terms of length of protection.

(c) Remember that the Tukey T method is appropriate to use only when significant differences in the means of the groups are found. First, we compute absolute differences $|\overline{X}_j - \overline{X}'_j|$ among all $\dfrac{c(c-1)}{2}$ pairs of means.

Since there are c = 3 groups, there are $\dfrac{3\,(3-1)}{2} = 3$ possible pairwise comparisons to be made:

1. $|\bar{X}_1 - \bar{X}_2| = |78.6 - 91.2| = 12.6$

2. $|\bar{X}_1 - \bar{X}_3| = |78.6 - 88.8| = 10.2$

3. $|\bar{X}_2 - \bar{X}_3| = |91.2 - 88.8| = 2.4$

Second, we calculate the critical range:

$$\text{critical range} \;=\; Q_{c,n-c}\left(\sqrt{\frac{MSW}{n_j}}\right)$$

$$=\; Q_{.05,3,12}\sqrt{\frac{5.23}{5}}$$

$$=\; (3.77)\,\sqrt{1.046}$$

$$=\; (3.77)\,(1.0223)$$

$$=\; 3.854$$

Third, we compare the absolute differences to the critical value. Since 12.6 > 3.854 and 10.2 > 3.854, we would conclude that there is a difference between Brand 1 and Brand 2 and Brand 1 and Brand 3.

II. A winery has developed four different methods for the production of its best white wine. The owner wants to rate the wine produced by each of these different methods. She decides that the wine produced by each method should be evaluated once by each of six different wine experts, who differ in terms of wine tasting experience. Each wine tester rates the wines on a scale from 0-100 (worst to best) with the following results:

Wine Tester	---------------------- Production Method ----------------------				
	A	B	C	D	Totals
1	47	34	59	47	187
2	55	47	64	51	217
3	52	42	67	56	217
4	59	38	73	53	223
5	61	46	71	56	234
6	56	41	78	61	236
Totals	330	248	412	324	1314

Using a .05 level of significance, is there evidence of a difference in the mean ratings of the wine by production methods?

SOLUTION

Use the randomized block design. The following information can be obtained from the table:

$$r = 6, \quad c = 4$$

$$X_{.1} = 330 \quad X_{.2} = 248 \quad X_{.3} = 412 \quad X_{.4} = 324$$

$$X_{1.} = 187 \quad X_{2.} = 217 \quad X_{3.} = 217 \quad X_{4.} = 223 \quad X_{5.} = 234 \quad X_{6.} = 236$$

$$GT = 1,314$$

$$\sum_{j=1}^{c} \sum_{i=1}^{r} X_{ij}^2 = 47^2 + 55^2 + \ldots + 61^2 = 74,778$$

$$\sum_{i=1}^{r} \frac{X_{i.}^2}{c} = \frac{187^2 + 217^2 + \ldots + 236^2}{4} = \frac{289,328}{4} = 72,332.00$$

$$\sum_{j=1}^{c} \frac{X_{.j}^2}{r} = \frac{330^2 + 248^2 + 412^2 + 324^2}{6} = \frac{445,124}{6} = 74,187.33$$

$$\frac{(GT)^2}{rc} = \frac{(1314)^2}{(6)\,(4)} = \frac{1,726,596}{24} = 71,941.50$$

Obtaining the sum of squares:

$$SST = \sum_{j=1}^{c} \sum_{i=1}^{r} X_{ij}^2 - \frac{(GT)^2}{rc} = 74,778 - 71,941.50 = 2,836.50$$

$$SSTR = \sum_{j=1}^{c} \frac{X_{.j}^2}{r} - \frac{(GT)^2}{rc} = 74,187.33 - 71,941.50 = 2,245.83$$

$$SSBL = \sum_{i=1}^{r} \frac{X_{i.}^2}{c} - \frac{(GT)^2}{rc} = 72,332.00 - 71,941.50 = 390.50$$

$$SSE = \sum_{j=1}^{c} \sum_{i=1}^{r} X_{ij}^2 - \sum_{j=1}^{c} \frac{X_{.j}^2}{r} - \sum_{i=1}^{r} \frac{X_{i.}^2}{c} + \frac{(GT)^2}{rc} =$$

$$= 74,778.00 - 74,187.33 - 72.332.00 + 71,941.50 =$$
$$= 200.17$$

Obtaining the mean squares (i.e., variances):

$$MSTR = \frac{SSTR}{c-1} = \frac{2245.83}{4-1} = 748.61$$

$$MSBL = \frac{SSBL}{r-1} = \frac{390.50}{6-1} = 78.10$$

$$MSE = \frac{SSE}{(r-1)\,(c-1)} = \frac{200.17}{(6-1)\,(4-1)} = \frac{200.17}{15} = 13.345$$

To test the null hypothesis that population mean ratings are the same for all production methods, we calculate the following:

H_0: $\mu_A = \mu_B = \mu_C = \mu_D$

H_1: Not all μ_j are equal.

$$F_{(c-1),(r-1)(c-1)} = \frac{MSTR}{MSE} = \frac{748.61}{13.345} = 56.097$$

Using $\alpha = .05$, we compare this to our critical value:

$$F_{(c-1),(r-1)(c-1)} = F_{3,15} = 3.29$$

Since $F = 56.097 > 3.29$, we reject H_0. At the .05 level of significance there is evidence that there are differences among the production methods with respect to the flavor of the wine produced.

ANALYSIS OF VARIANCE TABLE
FOR THE RANDOMIZED BLOCK DESIGN

Source	Sum of Squares	Degrees of Freedom	Mean Square Variance	F
Among Treatments (production methods)	2,245.83	$4 - 1 = 3$	748.61	56.097
Among Blocks (wine tasters)	390.50	$6 - 1 = 5$	78.10	5.85
Error	200.17	$(6-1)(4-1)=15$	13.345	
Total	2,836.50	$(6)(4) - 1 = 23$		

III. The marketing research department of an advertising agency wants to study the effect of color and type of print on the amount of time spent reading an advertisement for a new perfume. The color combinations to be studied were: black-white, yellow-orange, and blue-gold. Two types of print were also studied: all capital letters and upper-lower case letters. A group of 24 women was randomly assigned a color combination and a print type. The time (in seconds) spent reading the ad was recorded with the following results:

Type of Print	Black-White	Yellow-Orange	Blue-Gold	Totals
	----------------------	Color Combinations	----------------------	
All Caps	25	32	34	
	22	25	33	328
	24	30	28	
	19	29	27	
Upper-Lower Case	35	50	42	
	32	45	38	471
	31	43	37	
	30	47	41	
Totals	218	301	280	799

At the .05 level of significance

(a) Is there an effect due to type of print?
(b) Is there an effect due to color combination?
(c) Is there an interaction between type of print and color combination?

SOLUTION

Let A = Type of Print
   B = Color Combination

Referring to the table above we have:

$$r = 2 \quad c = 3 \quad n = 4$$

$$X_{1..} = 328 \qquad X_{2..} = 471$$

$$X_{.1.} = 218 \qquad X_{.2.} = 301 \qquad X_{.3.} = 280$$

$$X_{11.} = 90 \qquad X_{12.} = 116 \qquad X_{13.} = 122$$

$$X_{21.} = 128 \qquad X_{22.} = 185 \qquad X_{23.} = 158$$

$$GT = 799$$

$$\sum_{i=1}^{r} \sum_{j=1}^{c} \sum_{k=1}^{n} X_{ijk}^2 = 25^2 + 22^2 + 24^2 + \ldots + 41^2 = 28{,}145$$

$$\sum_{i=1}^{r} \frac{X_{i..}^2}{cn} = \frac{328^2 + 471^2}{(3)(4)} = \frac{107{,}584 + 221{,}841}{12} = \frac{329{,}425}{12}$$
$$= 27{,}452.083$$

$$\sum_{j=1}^{c} \frac{X_{.j.}^2}{rn} = \frac{218^2 + 301^2 + 280^2}{(2)(4)} = \frac{47{,}524 + 90{,}601 + 78{,}400}{8}$$
$$= \frac{216{,}525}{8} = 27{,}065.625$$

$$\sum_{i=1}^{r} \sum_{j=1}^{c} \frac{X_{ij.}^2}{n} = \frac{90^2 + 128^2 + 116^2 + \ldots + 158^2}{4} = \frac{112{,}013}{4}$$
$$= 28{,}003.25$$

$$\frac{(GT)^2}{rcn} = \frac{799^2}{(2)\ (3)\ (4)} = \frac{638,401}{24} = 26,600.042$$

Obtaining the sum of squares:

$$SST = \sum_{i=1}^{r} \sum_{j=1}^{c} \sum_{k=1}^{n} X_{ijk}^{2} - \frac{(GT)^2}{rcn} = 28,145 - 26,600.042$$
$$= 1,544,958$$

$$SSFA = \sum_{i=1}^{r} \frac{X_{i..}^{2}}{cn} - \frac{(GT)^2}{rcn} = 27,452.083 - 26,600.042 = 852.041$$

$$SSFB = \sum_{j=1}^{c} \frac{X_{.j.}^{2}}{rn} - \frac{(GT)^2}{rcn} = 27,065.625 - 26,600.042 = 465,583$$

$$SSAB = \sum_{i=1}^{r} \sum_{j=1}^{c} \frac{X_{ij.}^{2}}{n} - \sum_{i=1}^{r} \frac{X_{i..}^{2}}{cn} - \sum_{j=1}^{r} \frac{X_{.j.}^{2}}{rn} + \frac{(GT)^2}{rcn} =$$

$$= 28,003.25 - 27,452.083 - 27,065.625 + 26,600.042$$
$$= 85.583$$

$$SSE = \sum_{i=1}^{r} \sum_{j=1}^{c} \sum_{k=1}^{n} X_{ijk}^{2} - \sum_{i=1}^{r} \sum_{j=1}^{c} \frac{X_{ij.}^{2}}{n}$$

$$= 28,145 - 28,003.25$$
$$= 141.750$$

Obtaining the mean squares (i.e., variances):

$$MSA = \frac{SSFA}{r - 1} = \frac{852.041}{2 - 1} = 852.041$$

$$\text{MSB} \quad = \frac{\text{SSFB}}{c-1} = \frac{465.583}{3-1} = 232.792$$

$$\text{MSAB} = \frac{\text{SSAB}}{(r-1)\,(c-1)} = \frac{85.583}{(2-1)\,(3-1)} = 42.792$$

$$\text{MSE} \quad = \frac{\text{SSE}}{rc\,(n-1)} = \frac{141.750}{(2)\,(3)\,(4-1)} = 7.875$$

This information may be presented in an Analysis of Variance Summary Table:

ANALYSIS OF VARIANCE SUMMARY TABLE

Source	Sum of Squares	Degrees of Freedom	Mean Square Variance	F
Type of print	852.041	1	852.041	108.20
Color combination	465.583	2	232.792	29.56
Type of print * Color Combination	85.584	2	42.792	5.43
Error	141.750	18	7.875	
Total	1544.958	23		

(a) At the .05 level of significance, the critical value for the test on the type of print is $F_{(1,18)} = 4.41$. Since $F_{(1,18)} = 108.20 > 4.41$, we reject H_0 and conclude that there is evidence of a difference between types of print in terms of the time spent in reading the ad.

(b) At the .05 level of significance, the critical value for the test on the color combination is $F_{(2,18)} = 3.55$. Since $F_{(2,18)} = 29.56 > 3.55$, we reject H_0 and conclude that there is evidence of a difference between color combinations in terms of the time spent in reading the ad.

(c) At the .05 level of significance, the critical value for the test on the type of print and the color combination interaction is $F_{(2,18)} = 3.55$. Since $F_{(2,18)} = 5.43 > 3.55$, we reject H_0 and conclude that there is evidence of a significant interaction effect between the type of print and the color combination.

Since the interaction effect in (c) is significant, we must interpret our main effects in (a) and (b) cautiously. Examining the data permits us to keep conclusion (a), but we must be careful about conclusion (b) in light of the interaction.

REVIEW PROBLEM

I. Samples of detergent produced by three different manufacturers were tested for how many dishes could be washed with one ounce of soap. The results were as follows:

Brand A	Brand B	Brand C
50	32	28
63	41	32
57	34	34
54	37	39
61	43	30
52	30	35

(a) At the .05 level of significance, is there evidence of a difference in the variances of the number of dishes washed by these three brands of detergent?

(b) At the .05 level of significance, is there evidence of a difference in the average number of dishes washed by these three brands of detergent?

SOLUTION

(a) H_0: $\sigma_1^2 = \sigma_2^2 = \sigma_3^2$
    H_1: Not all σ_j^2 are equal (j=1,2,3)
    $\alpha = .05$

Decision rule:

   Reject H_0 if $F_{MAX(3,5)} = 10.8$
   Otherwise, don't reject H_0.

Brand A	Brand B	Brand C
50	32	28
63	41	32
57	34	34
54	37	39
61	43	30
52	30	35

T_j	337	217	198	$GT = \sum_{j=1}^{3} T_j = 752$
n_j	6	6	6	$n = \sum_{j=1}^{3} n_j = 18$
$\bar{X}_j$	56.17	36.17	33.00	
T_j^2	113,569	47,089	39,204	$(GT)^2 = 565,504$
$\dfrac{T_j^2}{n_j}$	18,928.17	7,848.17	6,534	$\dfrac{(GT)^2}{n} = 31,416.89$
$\sum_{i=1}^{n_j} X_{ij}^2$	19,059	7,979	6,610	$\sum_{j=1}^{3} \dfrac{T_j^2}{n_j} = 33,310.34$
S_j^2	26.17	26.17	15.2	$\sum_{j=1}^{3} \sum_{i=1}^{n_j} X_{ij}^2 = 33,648$

Test statistic:

$$F_{MAX(3,5)} = \frac{26.17}{15.2} = 1.722$$

Conclusion:

Since $F_{MAX(3,5)} = 1.722 < 10.8$, do not reject H_0. There is no evidence of a difference in the variances of these three brands of detergent.

(b) H_0: $\mu_1 = \mu_2 = \mu_3$
   H_1: Not all the means are equal.
   $\alpha = .05$

Decision rule:

Reject H_0 if $F_{(2,15)} > 3.68$
Otherwise, do not reject H_0.

Sample results and test statistic:

$$\text{SSB} = \sum_{j=1}^{c} \frac{T_j^2}{n_j} - \frac{(GT)^2}{n} = 33{,}310.34 - 31{,}416.89 = 1{,}893.45$$

$$\text{SSW} = \sum_{j=1}^{c} \sum_{i=1}^{n_j} X_{ij}^2 - \sum_{j=1}^{c} \frac{T_j^2}{n_j} = 33{,}648 - 33{,}310.34 = 337.66$$

$$\text{SST} = \sum_{j=1}^{c} \sum_{i=1}^{n_j} X_{ij}^2 - \frac{(GT)^2}{n} = 33{,}648 - 31{,}416.89 = 2{,}231.11$$

ANALYSIS OF VARIANCE TABLE

Source	Sum of Squares	Degrees of Freedom	Mean Square Variance	F
Between Brands	1,893.45	$c - 1 =$ $3 - 1 = 2$	$\text{MSB} = \dfrac{1{,}893.45}{2}$ $= 946.725$	$F = \dfrac{946.725}{22.51}$ $= 42.06$
Within Brands	337.66	$n - c =$ $18 - 3 = 15$	$\text{MSW} = \dfrac{337.66}{15}$ $= 22.51$	
Total	2,231.11	$n - 1 =$ $18 - 1 = 17$		

Conclusion:

Reject H_0 since $42.06 > 3.68$. There is a significant difference in the average number of dishes washed by these three brands of detergent.

15

Nonparametric Methods

In Chapters 11–14 the so-called "classical methods" of hypothesis testing were described. Nevertheless, a problem of frequent concern to the researcher in the social sciences and in business is what kinds of testing procedures to choose from if (a) it is deemed inappropriate to make the more rigorous assumptions of the aforementioned classical methods; (b) the measurements attained on the data are only qualitative or in ranks; or (c) it is desired to treat such problems as randomness, trend, cyclical effects, symmetry or goodness of fit rather than testing hypotheses about particular population parameters. Hence, for such situations as these, a set of nonparametric procedures were devised. This chapter, then, focuses on the development of nonparametric methods of hypothesis testing. In particular, seven useful procedures are discussed: (1) the Wald-Wolfowitz one-sample runs test for randomness; (2) the Wilcoxon one-sample signed-ranks test; (3) the Wilcoxon paired-sample signed-ranks test; (4) the Wilcoxon rank sum test; (5) the Kruskal-Wallis test for C independent samples; (6) the Friedman rank test; and (7) Spearman's rank correlation procedure. In addition, numerous concepts such as levels of measurement, robustness, randomness, runs, trend, signs and power are discussed.

MULTIPLE CHOICE

1. The classification of various business firms into particular industrial groups is an example of

    a. a ratio scale.
    b. an interval scale.
    c. an ordinal scale.
    d. a nominal scale.

2. A consecutive series of similar items in a test for randomness is known as

    a. a sign.
    b. a robust procedure.
    c. an absolute normal score.
    d. a run.

3. In performing the Wilcoxon one-sample signed ranks test, absolute difference scores of zero

    a. are discarded.
    b. are given the rank +1.
    c. are given the rank –1.
    d. do not occur in practice.

4. The sum of the first n consecutive ranks (integers) is

    a. $\dfrac{n\,(n-1)}{4}$

    b. $\sqrt{\dfrac{n\,(n+1)\,(2n+1)}{24}}$

    c. $\dfrac{n\,(n+1)}{2}$

    d. None of the above.

5. The Wilcoxon paired-sample signed-ranks test is a nonparametric analogue of the

    a. χ^2 test for independence.
    b. runs test for randomness.
    c. analysis of variance F test.
    d. t test for related samples.

6. As the sample sizes in each of the C groups gets large, the Kruskal-Wallis test statistic H may be approximated by

   a. Z.
   b. $\chi^2_{(C-1)}$.
   c. $t_{(C-1)}$.
   d. $F_{(1,C-1)}$.

EXAMPLES

I. The manager of a paint store claims that 10 one-gallon cans of paint are mismatched for the requested color per week. A random sample of 15 weeks is chosen and the number of cans of mismatched paint is recorded below. Using a .05 level of significance, is there evidence to believe that the median number of mismatches is 10?

Number of mismatches (X_i): 5, 16, 4, 2, 11, 7, 3, 10, 0, 6, 9, 1, 9, 3, 8.

SOLUTION

We use the Wilcoxon one-sample signed-ranks test.

   H_0: Median = 10 mismatches
   H_1: Median $\neq$ 10 mismatches
   α = .05

Decision rule:

   Since $n \leq 20$ use the table of lower and upper critical values of W of the Wilcoxon signed-ranks test to obtain critical values for the test statistic W. Reject H_0 if $W \leq 21$ or if $W \geq 84$. Otherwise, do not reject H_0.

Sample result and test statistic:

X_i	$D_i = X_i - 10$	$\lvert D_i \rvert$	R_i	Sign of D_i
5	−5	5	7	−
16	6	6	8.5	+
4	−6	6	8.5	−
2	−8	8	12	−
11	1	1	2	+
7	−3	3	5	−
3	−7	7	10.5	−
10	0	−	−	Discard
0	−10	10	14	−
6	−4	4	6	−
9	−1	1	2	−
1	−9	9	13	−
9	−1	1	2	−
3	−7	7	10.5	−
8	−2	2	4	−

$$W = \sum_{i=1}^{14} R_i^+ = 8.5 + 2 = 10.5$$

Conclusion:

Since $W = 10.5 < 21$, we reject H_0 at the .05 level of significance. The median number of mismatches appears to be lower than 10.

II. Random samples of 14 Brand X room deodorizers and 12 Brand Y room deodorizers were obtained for experimental purposes. Recorded below are the days that the active ingredient in each product lasted:

X: 42, 44, 45, 47, 52, 53, 57, 68, 69, 72, 79, 81, 88, 94
Y: 51, 60, 64, 75, 80, 86, 97, 100, 120, 128, 136, 137

At the .01 level of significance, is there any significant difference in the length of effectiveness between Brand X and Brand Y room deodorizers?

SOLUTION

We use the Wilcoxon rank sum test for the difference between two mutually independent sample groups drawn from the same population or identical populations.

H_0: $M_1 = M_2$ (The median lengths of effectiveness are equal.)

H_1: $M_1 \neq M_2$ (The median lengths of effectiveness are not equal.)

$\alpha = .01$

Decision rule:

Since n_1 and n_2 are > 10, the test statistic T_{n_1} is approximately normally distributed.

Therefore, reject H_0 if $Z > 2.58$
            or if $Z < -2.58$
Otherwise, don't reject H_0.

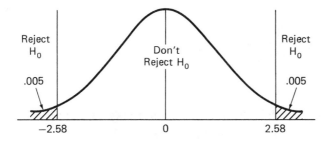

Sample results:

Lengths of Effectiveness (days)		Combined Rankings of Lengths of Effectiveness for X and Y	
X	Y	X	Y
42	51	1	5
44	60	2	9
45	64	3	10
47	75	4	14
52	80	6	16
53	86	7	18
57	97	8	21
68	100	11	22
69	120	12	23
72	128	13	24
79	136	15	25
81	137	17	26
88		19	
94		20	

$n_2 = 14$ $\qquad$ $n_1 = 12$ $\qquad$ $T_2 = 138$ $\qquad$ $T_1 = 213$

Test statistic: $\quad Z \cong \dfrac{T_1 - \mu_{T_1}}{\sigma_{T_1}}$

where

T_1 = the summation of the ranks assigned to the n_1 observations in the smaller sample = 213

μ_{T_1} = the mean value of $T_1 = \dfrac{n_1 (n + 1)}{2} = \dfrac{12 (27)}{2} = 162$

σ_{T_1} = the standard deviation of $T_1 = \sqrt{\dfrac{n_1 n_2 (n + 1)}{12}}$

$$= \sqrt{\frac{12\ (14)\ (27)}{12}} = \sqrt{378} = 19.4422$$

Thus, $Z \cong \dfrac{213 - 162}{19.4422} = \dfrac{51}{19.4422} = 2.62$

Conclusion:

Since $Z = 2.62 > 2.58$, we reject H_0. There is evidence of a significant difference between the lengths of effectiveness of the two brands (X and Y) at the .01 level of significance.

III. An educational service claims that students can improve their scores on a standardized exam by taking a special course. The exam scores of a sample of 8 students before and after the course are presented below:

Student	Before	After
1	62	70
2	69	67
3	71	86
4	58	77
5	75	75
6	68	81
7	60	80
8	72	82

At the .05 level of significance, is there evidence to conclude that a student's exam score improved after taking this course?

SOLUTION

We use the Wilcoxon paired-sample signed-ranks test.

H_0: $M_D \leq 0$ (Median score does not improve after course.)
H_1: $M_D > 0$ (Median score does improve after course.)
$\alpha = .05$

Decision rule:

Since $n \leq 20$ use the table of lower and upper critical values W of the Wilcoxon signed-ranks test to obtain critical values for the test statistic W. Reject H_0 if $W \geq 25$. Otherwise, do not reject H_0.

Sample results:

Student	Before	After	D_i = After – Before	$|D_i|$	R_i	Sign of D_i
1	62	70	8	8	2	+
2	69	67	–2	2	1	–
3	71	86	15	15	5	+
4	58	77	19	19	6	+
5	75	75	0	--	--	Discard
6	68	81	13	13	4	+
7	60	80	20	20	7	+
8	72	82	10	10	3	+

Test statistic:

$$W = \sum_{i=1}^{n} R_i^+$$

where
n = number of pairs minus any pairs whose D_i is zero = 7

$$\sum_{i=1}^{n} R_i^+ = \text{sum of the positive ranks}$$

$$\text{Thus, } W = \sum_{i=1}^{7} R_i^+ = 2 + 5 + 6 + 4 + 7 + 3 = 27$$

Conclusion:

Since $W = 27 > 25$, we reject H_0 at the .05 level of significance. There is evidence that the course improves exam scores.

IV. An industrial psychologist wants to evaluate different styles of management based on level of productivity. Eighteen employees of a telephone manufacturing company are chosen at random and assigned in groups of six to each of three styles of management (authoritarian, democratic, or laissez-faire). At the .05 level of significance, do the different styles of management have an effect on the average number of telephones assembled? The number of telephones assembled by employees under the different styles of management are as follows:

MANAGEMENT STYLE		
Authoritarian I	Democratic II	Laissez-Faire III
42	36	49
41	34	41
39	33	38
41	32	45
37	40	37
40	35	42

SOLUTION

We use the Kruskal-Wallis test for 3 independent samples.

H_0: $M_I = M_{II} = M_{III}$ (The median number of telephones assembled by employees under the three management styles are equal.)

H_1: Not all medians are equal.

$\alpha = .05$

Decision rule:

Since all n_j's > 5, the test statistic H may be approximated by the χ^2 distribution with $C - 1$ (or $3 - 1 = 2$) degrees of freedom. Thus, reject H_0 if $H > 5.991$. Otherwise, don't reject H_0.

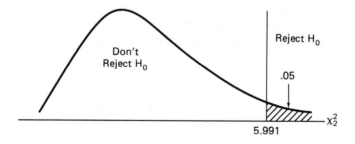

Sample results:

Number of Telephones Assembled			Conversion of Number of Telephones Assembled to Ranks		
I	II	III	I	II	III
42	36	49	15.5	5	18
41	34	41	13	3	13
39	33	38	9	2	8
41	32	45	13	1	17
37	40	37	6.5	10.5	6.5
40	35	42	10.5	4	15.5
			$T_1 = 67.5$	$T_2 = 25.5$	$T_3 = 78$

Test statistic:

$$H = \left[\frac{12}{n\,(n+1)} \left(\sum_{j=1}^{C} \frac{T_j^2}{n_j} \right) \right] - 3\,(n+1)$$

$$= \left[\frac{12}{18\,(18+1)} \left(\sum_{j=1}^{3} \frac{T_j^2}{n_j} \right) \right] - 3\,(18+1)$$

$$= \left[\frac{12}{342} \left(\frac{(67.5)^2}{6} + \frac{(25.5)^2}{6} + \frac{(78)^2}{6} \right) \right] - 3\,(19)$$

$$= \frac{12}{342}\,(1881.75) - 57 = 66.026 - 57 = 9.026$$

Conclusion: Since the computed value of the test statistic $H = 9.026 > 5.991$, we reject H_0 at the .05 level of significance. The industrial psychologist may conclude that at least two of the management styles are different with respect to the median number of telephones assembled.

V. A marketing research firm is conducting a study to determine differences in four kinds of pickles. Nine people are asked to rate the pickles on a 5-point scale (1 = very bad, 5 = very good) for four characteristics: crispness, tartness, color, and spiciness. The table below shows the summated ratings accumulated over all four characteristics.

SUMMATED RATINGS OF FOUR KINDS OF PICKLES

Rater	--------------------Kind of Pickles--------------------			
	Brand A	Brand B	Brand C	Brand D
1	15	18	20	20
2	16	15	17	18
3	17	17	18	19
4	20	10	20	12
5	11	14	13	18
6	15	15	12	17
7	18	20	19	17
8	16	13	12	15
9	14	11	15	16

(a) Convert the data to ranks.
(b) Test the null hypothesis that the median summated rating scores for the four kinds of pickles are equal. (*Remember:* Your alternative hypothesis will test if at least two of the kinds of pickles have median summated rating scores which differ.)

Use the $\alpha = .05$ level of significance.

SOLUTION

(a)

CONVERTING THE DATA TO RANKS

Rater	----------------Kind of Pickles----------------			
	Brand A	Brand B	Brand C	Brand D
1	1.0	2.0	3.5	3.5
2	2.0	1.0	3.0	4.0
3	1.5	1.5	3.0	4.0
4	3.5	1.0	3.5	2.0
5	1.0	3.0	2.0	4.0
6	2.5	2.5	1.0	4.0
7	2.0	4.0	3.0	1.0
8	4.0	2.0	1.0	3.0
9	2.0	1.0	3.0	4.0
Rank Totals	19.5	18.0	23.0	29.5

Use Friedman Rank Test for c related samples.

(b) H_0: $M_A = M_B = M_C = M_D$ (There is no difference in the ratings of these pickles.)

      H_1: Not all M_j's are equal   (Where j = Brand A, Brand B, Brand C, Brand D.)

      $\alpha = .05$

      We check the rankings:

$$R_{.1} + R_{.2} + R_{.3} + R_{.4} = \frac{n\,c\,(c+1)}{2}$$

From the above data:

$$19.5 + 18.0 + 23.0 + 29.5 \; = \; \frac{9\,(4)\,(5)}{2}$$

$$90 = 90$$

Using the Friedman rank test statistic:

$$F_R = \frac{12}{n\,c\,(c+1)} \sum_{j=1}^{C} R_{.j}^2 - 3n\,(c+1)$$

$$= \frac{12}{9\,(4)\,(5)} \,[19.5^2 + 18.0^2 + 23.0^2 + 29.5^2] - 3\,(9)\,(5)$$

$$= \frac{12}{180}\,[2103.5] - 135$$

$$= 140.233 - 135$$

$$= 5.233$$

Since the computed F_R statistic (5.233) does not exceed the critical value ($\chi_3^2 = 7.815$), we do not reject the null hypothesis at the .05 level of significance. There is no evidence, with respect to the pickles, of a difference in their median ratings.

VI. The Human Resources Department of a drug company was interested in determining whether there was a relationship between a salesperson's years of experience and sales (in thousands of dollars) for a given period of time. A sample of 9 employees was selected with the following results:

Employee	1	2	3	4	5	6	7	8	9
Years of Experience (X)	11	13	7	12	10	9	14	16	8
Sales (Y)	8	14	5	7	10	15	13	11	9

Measure the rank correlation between sales and the number of years of experience. Is there evidence of a relationship at the .01 level of significance?

SOLUTION

We use the Spearman rank correlation (denoted r_s).

> H_0:   There is no relationship between sales and years of experience.
> H_1:   There is a relationship between sales and years of experience.
> $\alpha = .01$

Decision rule:

> Reject H_0 if $Z < -2.58$
>   or if $Z > 2.58$
> Otherwise, do not reject H_0.

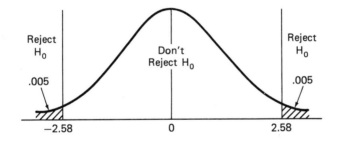

Sample results:

Employee	Years of Experience (X)	Sales (Y)	Rank R_X	R_Y	d_R	d_R^2
1	11	8	5	3	2	4
2	13	14	7	8	−1	1
3	7	5	1	1	0	0
4	12	7	6	2	4	16
5	10	10	4	5	−1	1
6	9	15	3	9	−6	36
7	14	13	8	7	1	1
8	16	11	9	6	3	9
9	8	9	2	4	−2	4

$$\sum d_{R_i}^2 = 72$$

Test statistic:

$$Z \cong r_s \sqrt{n - 1}$$

where

$$r_s = 1 - \frac{6 \sum_{i=1}^{n} d_{R_i}^2}{n\,(n^2 - 1)} = 1 - \frac{6\,(72)}{9\,(9^2 - 1)}$$

$$= 1 - \frac{432}{9\,(81 - 1)} = 1 - \frac{432}{720}$$

$$r_s = 1 - .60 = .40$$

Thus, $Z \cong .40 \sqrt{9-1} = .40 \ (2.8284) = 1.13$

Conclusion:

Since $Z \cong 1.13$ falls between the critical Z values ($-2.58 \leq Z \leq 2.58$), we cannot reject the null hypothesis at the .01 level of significance. There is no evidence that there is a relationship between sales and years of experience.

REVIEW PROBLEMS

I. In a pretest of a questionnaire, a group of seven interviewers recorded the time that the interview took. The number of minutes recorded were: 17, 13, 15, 18, 20, 10 and 16. Is there evidence to believe that the median is more than 14 at the .05 level of significance?

SOLUTION

Use the Wilcoxon one-sample signed-ranks test.

H_0: Median ≤ 14 minutes
H_1: Median > 14 minutes
$\alpha = .05$

Decision rule:

Using the table of critical values, reject H_0 if $W \geq 25$. Otherwise, don't reject H_0.

Sample result and test statistic:

Interview #	X_i	$D_i = X_i - 14$	$|D_i|$	R_i	Sign of D_i
1	17	3	3	4	+
2	13	−1	1	1.5	−
3	15	1	1	1.5	+
4	18	4	4	5.5	+
5	20	6	6	7	+
6	10	−4	4	5.5	−
7	16	2	2	3	+

$$W = \sum_{i=1}^{7} R_i^+ = 4 + 1.5 + 5.5 + 7 + 3 = 21$$

Conclusion:

Since $W = 21$ is less than the critical value (25), we don't reject H_0. There is no evidence to conclude that the median is more than 14 minutes at the .05 level of significance.

II. A manufacturer of microwave ovens wants to determine if there is a difference in the way that two of its models pop corn. The following data show the number of kernels left unpopped in each of the two microwave models:

Model I	Model II
27	41
18	25
12	20
28	27
11	29
15	18
21	31

At the .05 level of significance, do the two models differ significantly in their ability to pop corn?

SOLUTION

We use the Wilcoxon rank sum test.

H_0: $M_1 = M_2$ (Median number of unpopped kernels is equal.)
H_1: $M_1 \neq M_2$ (Median number of unpopped kernels is different.)
$\alpha = .05$

Decision rule:

Since both n_1 and n_2 are ≤ 10, lower and upper critical values for the rank sum test statistic T_1 are obtained. Hence, we reject H_0 if $T_1 \leq 36$ or if $T_1 \geq 69$. Otherwise, don't reject H_0.

Sample result and test statistic:

Unpopped Kernels		Conversion of Unpopped Kernels to Ranks	
Model I	Model II	Model I	Model II
27	41	9.5	14
18	25	4.5	8
12	20	2	6
28	27	11	9.5
11	29	1	12
15	18	3	4.5
21	31	7	13
		$T_1 = 38$	$T_2 = 67$

Conclusion:

Since the observed value $T_1 = 38$ falls between the critical values 36 and 69, H_0 cannot be rejected at the .05 level of significance. It may be concluded that there is no evidence of any significant differences between the two models with respect to popping.

III. An office manager must decide between two types of printers for the office. He has narrowed his choice to two different models. In making his decision, he runs the same report through both models and records the time (in minutes) it takes to print the report. His results show the following:

Model	Report								
	1	2	3	4	5	6	7	8	9
I	8.9	8.7	8.8	5.8	6.3	11.0	7.8	10.0	9.1
II	13.3	10.5	12.5	7.2	9.1	9.1	7.8	10.9	10.2

At the .05 level of significance, is there a difference in printing time between the two models?

SOLUTION

We use the Wilcoxon paired-sample signed-ranks test.

H_0: $M_D = 0$ (There is no difference in the time it takes to print a report.)
H_1: $M_D \neq 0$ (There is a difference in the time it takes to print a report.)
$\alpha = .05$

Decision rule:

Reject H_0 if $W \leq 3$ or if $W \geq 33$. Otherwise, do not reject H_0.

Sample results:

Report	Printer I	Printer II	$D_i = I - II$	$|D_i|$	R_i	Sign of D_i
1	8.9	13.3	−4.4	4.4	8	−
2	8.7	10.5	−1.8	1.8	4	−
3	8.8	12.5	−3.7	3.7	7	−
4	5.8	7.2	−1.4	1.4	3	−
5	6.3	9.1	−2.8	2.8	6	−
6	11.0	9.1	1.9	1.9	5	+
7	7.8	7.8	0	--	--	Discard
8	10.0	10.9	−.9	.9	1	−
9	9.1	10.2	−1.1	1.1	2	−

Test statistic:

$$W = \sum_{i=1}^{n} R_i^+ = 5$$

Conclusion:

Since $W = 5$ falls between the critical values ($3 < W < 33$), we do not reject H_0. There is no evidence of a significant difference between the two printers with respect to the median time it takes to print a report.

IV. A marketing vice president for an insurance company wants to determine whether or not three selling pitches have identical effects upon the number of insurance policies sold. The number of policies sold using each of these approaches is shown below:

I	II	III
425	470	398
391	475	440
443	709	452
412	578	488
377	495	460
395	510	428
406		

At the .01 level of significance, is there a difference between the three different selling pitches with respect to the number of insurance policies sold?

SOLUTION

We use the Kruskal-Wallis test.

H_0: $M_1 = M_2 = M_3$
H_1: Not all the medians are equal.
$\alpha = .01$

Decision rule:

Using the χ^2 approximation to the test statistic H, we reject H_0 if $H > 9.210$. Otherwise, do not reject H_0.

Sample results:

I	II	III	Combined Ranks I	Combined Ranks II	Combined Ranks III
425	470	398	7	13	4
391	475	440	2	14	9
443	709	452	10	19	11
412	578	488	6	18	15
377	495	460	1	16	12
395	510	428	3	17	8
406			5		
			$T_1 = 34$	$T_2 = 97$	$T_3 = 59$

Test statistic:

$$H = \left[\frac{12}{n\,(n+1)} \left(\sum_{j=1}^{C} \frac{T_j^2}{n_j} \right) \right] - 3\,(n+1)$$

$$= \left[\frac{12}{19\,(19 + 1)} \left(\frac{(34)^2}{7} + \frac{(97)^2}{6} + \frac{(59)^2}{6} \right) \right] - 3\,(20)$$

$$= \frac{12}{380}\,(2{,}313.4763) - 60 = 73.057 - 60 = 13.057$$

Conclusion:

Since the computed value H = 13.057 > 9.21, we reject H_0 at the .01 level of significance. The marketing vice president may conclude that at least two of the selling pitches do not have identical effects upon the median number of policies sold.

V. A sports magazine wants to determine if there is a relationship between a football player's starting salary and the number of votes he received for most valuable player of the year. It takes a random sample of twelve players and collects the following data:

Player	Votes Received	Starting Salary (in thousands)
1	5	83
2	5	94
3	6	98
4	11	152
5	14	199
6	7	107
7	8	124
8	12	206
9	10	163
10	4	92
11	9	131
12	5	90

Measure the rank correlation between votes received and starting salary. Is there evidence of a significant relationship at the .05 level of significance?

SOLUTION

Use Spearman rank correlation.

      H_0:   There is no relationship between votes received and starting salary.
      H_1:   There is a relationship between votes received and starting salary.
      $\alpha = .05$

Decision rule:

      Reject H_0 if $Z < -1.96$ or if $Z > 1.96$.
      Otherwise, do not reject H_0.

Sample results:

Player	Votes Received (X)	Starting Salary (in thousands) (Y)	Rank R_X	R_Y	d_R	d_R^2
1	5	83	3	1	2	4
2	5	94	3	4	−1	1
3	6	98	5	5	0	0
4	11	152	10	9	1	1
5	14	199	12	11	1	1
6	7	107	6	6	0	0
7	8	124	7	7	0	0
8	12	206	11	12	−1	1
9	10	163	9	10	−1	1
10	4	92	1	3	−2	4
11	9	131	8	8	0	0
12	5	90	3	2	1	1

$$\sum_{i=1}^{12} d_{R_i}^2 = 14$$

Test statistic:

$$Z \cong r_s \sqrt{n-1}$$

where

$$r_s \cong 1 - \frac{6\Sigma d_{R_i}^2}{n\,(n^2-1)} = 1 - \frac{6\,(14)}{12(12^2-1)} = 1 - .049 = .951$$

Therefore, $Z \cong .951 \sqrt{12-1} = 3.15$

Conclusion:

Since $Z \cong 3.15 > 1.96$, we reject the null hypothesis at the .05 level of significance. There is evidence of a relationship between votes for most valuable player and starting salary.

16

The Simple Linear Regression Model and Correlation

In our discussion of various statistical methods, we have been primarily concerned with problems involving only a single variable of interest. In simple linear regression and correlation we will examine the relationship between two quantitative variables. Regression analysis utilizes one variable (the independent) for predicting another variable (the dependent), while correlation measures the strength of the association between the two variables. In regression analysis, the Least Squares method is used to determine the two regression coefficients: b_0, the Y intercept, and b_1, the slope. These regression coefficients can then be utilized to predict the value of the dependent variable. Once this prediction is obtained along with the standard error of the estimate (the measure of variation around the line of regression), statistical inference can be utilized to determine the significance of the relationship and to obtain confidence interval estimates. Moreover, residual analysis and other regression diagnostics can be used to evaluate the appropriateness of the developed regression model.

MULTIPLE CHOICE

1. The scatter diagram below shows

   a. a positive linear relationship.
   b. a positive curvilinear relationship.
   c. a negative linear relationship.
   d. no relationship between X and Y.

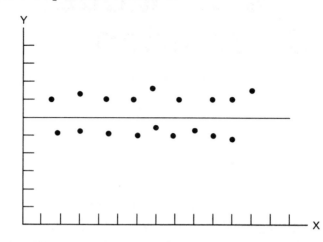

2. The idea of a "best fit" line means that we want to find the straight line for which the sum of squared differences between _____ are as small as possible.

   a. X_i and Y_i
   b. X_i and $\hat{Y}_i$
   c. $\overline{X}$ and $\overline{Y}$
   d. Y_i and $\hat{Y}_i$

3. The interpretation of the standard error of the estimate is analogous to that of the

   a. mean.
   b. standard deviation.
   c. slope.
   d. intercept.

4. $\displaystyle\sum_{i=1}^{n} (Y_i - \hat{Y}_i) =$ _____.

    a. 0
    b. 1
    c. S_{YX}
    d. r^2

5. The coefficient of determination measures

    a. the variability around the line of regression.
    b. homoscedasticity.
    c. the proportion of variation that is explained by the independent variable for the regression model.
    d. the portion of the dependent variable that varies with factors other than the independent variable.

6. If $b_0 = 27.23$, $b_1 = -16.52$, and $r^2 = .7921$, then r = _____.

    a. −1.65
    b. +.89
    c. −.89
    d. cannot be determined with this information.

7. Which of the following tests may be used to determine whether there is a significant linear relationship between X and Y?

    a. testing whether β_1 (the true slope) is equal to zero.
    b. setting up a confidence-interval estimate of β_1 and determining whether the hypothesized value ($\beta_1 = 0$) is included in that interval.
    c. testing whether ρ (the true correlation) between X and Y is equal to zero.
    d. All of the above.

8. The assumption of _____ requires that the variation around the line of regression be constant for all values of X.

   a. normality
   (b) homoscedasticity
   c. independence of error
   d. random selection

9. If SST = 315, and r^2 = .92, then SSR = _____ and SSE = _____.

   (a) 289.8; 25.2
   b. 25.2; 289.8
   c. 92; 100
   d. 100; 92

EXAMPLES

I. The following table shows how many weeks 10 interviewers have worked for a marketing research firm and the number of interviews each one conducted between 11 a.m. and 7 p.m. on a given day.

Interviewer #	1	2	3	4	5	6	7	8	9	10
Weeks of Experience	15	41	58	18	37	52	28	24	45	33
Number of Interviews Conducted	4	9	12	6	8	10	6	5	10	7

(a) Set up a scatter diagram.

(b) Assuming a linear relationship, use the Least Squares method to compute the regression coefficients (b_0 and b_1).

(c) Interpret the meaning of the intercept (b_0) and the slope (b_1) in this problem.

(d) Predict the number of interviews completed by an interviewer with 20 weeks of experience.

(e) Compute the standard error of the estimate.

(f) Compute the coefficient of determination (r^2) and interpret its meaning in this problem.

(g) Compute the coefficient of correlation (r).

(h) Compute the adjusted r^2.

(i) At the .05 level of significance, is there a relationship between number of interviews and weeks of experience?

(j) Set up a 95% confidence interval estimate of the average number of interviews completed for interviewers with 20 weeks of experience.

(k) Set up a 95% interval estimate of number of interviews completed for an individual interviewer with 20 weeks of experience.

(l) Set up the 95% confidence interval estimate of the true slope.

(m) Discuss why you shouldn't predict number of interviews completed for interviewers who have less than 15 weeks of experience or more than 58 weeks of experience.

SOLUTION

Basic Computations:

Interviewer #	X_i Weeks of Experience	Y_i Number of Interviews Completed	X_i^2	Y_i^2	X_iY_i
1	15	4	225	16	60
2	41	9	1,691	81	369
3	58	12	3,364	144	696
4	18	6	324	36	108
5	37	8	1,369	64	296
6	52	10	2,704	100	520
7	28	6	784	36	168
8	24	5	576	25	120
9	45	10	2,025	100	450
10	33	7	1,089	49	231
	351	77	14,141	651	3,018
	$\sum_{i=1}^{10} X_i$	$\sum_{i=1}^{10} Y_i$	$\sum_{i=1}^{10} X_i^2$	$\sum_{i=1}^{10} Y_i^2$	$\sum_{i=1}^{10} X_iY_i$

$$\overline{X} = 35.1 \qquad \overline{Y} = 7.7$$

(a) Scatter diagram of Weeks of Experience versus Number of Interviews Completed

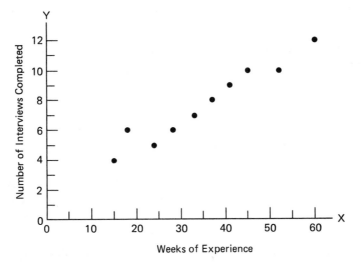

Weeks of Experience

(b) Regression coefficients.

$$b_1 = \frac{n\sum_{i=1}^{n} X_i Y_i - \left(\sum_{i=1}^{n} X_i\right)\left(\sum_{i=1}^{n} Y_i\right)}{n\sum_{i=1}^{n} X_i^2 - \left(\sum_{i=1}^{n} X_i\right)^2}$$

$$= \frac{(10)(3{,}018) - (351)(77)}{(10)(14{,}141) - (351)^2}$$

$$= \frac{30{,}180 - 27{,}027}{141{,}410 - 123{,}201} = \frac{3{,}153}{18{,}209} = .173$$

$$b_0 = \overline{Y} - b_1\overline{X} = 7.7 - (.173)(35.1) = 7.7 - 6.07 = 1.63$$

$$\hat{Y}_i = 1.63 + .173 X_i$$

(c) The intercept in this problem is 1.63. The Y intercept represents the value of Y when X equals zero. We can interpret this as the portion of completed interviews that varies with factors other than weeks of experience. The slope in this problem is .173. This means that for each unit increase in weeks of experience, the number of completed interviews will increase by .173 units.

(d) Predict the number of interviews completed by an interviewer with 20 weeks of experience.

$$\hat{Y}_i = b_0 + b_1 X_i$$

$$= 1.63 + (.173)(20) = 1.63 + 3.46$$

$$= 5.09. \qquad \text{The predicted average number of interviews completed is } 5.09 \text{ when an interviewer has 20 weeks of experience.}$$

(e) Standard error of estimate, $S_{YX} = \sqrt{\dfrac{\text{Unexplained Sum of Squares}}{n-2}}$

$$S_{YX} \qquad \sqrt{\dfrac{\displaystyle\sum_{i=1}^{n} Y_i^2 - b_0 \sum_{i=1}^{n} Y_i - b_1 \sum_{i=1}^{n} X_i Y_i}{n-2}}$$

$$= \sqrt{\dfrac{651 - (1.63)(77) - (.173)(3018)}{10-2}}$$

$$= \sqrt{\dfrac{3.376}{8}}$$

$$= \sqrt{.422}$$

$$= .6496$$

(f) Coefficient of determination, $r^2 = \dfrac{\text{Explained Sum of Squares}}{\text{Total Sum of Squares}}$

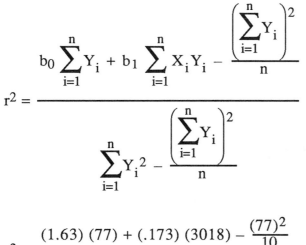

$$r^2 = \frac{b_0 \sum_{i=1}^{n} Y_i + b_1 \sum_{i=1}^{n} X_i Y_i - \dfrac{\left(\sum_{i=1}^{n} Y_i\right)^2}{n}}{\sum_{i=1}^{n} Y_i^2 - \dfrac{\left(\sum_{i=1}^{n} Y_i\right)^2}{n}}$$

$$r^2 = \frac{(1.63)(77) + (.173)(3018) - \dfrac{(77)^2}{10}}{651 - \dfrac{(77)^2}{10}}$$

$$= \frac{54.724}{58.1} = .9419$$

Interpretation:

> For this example, 94.19% of the variation in completed interviews can be explained by variability in weeks of experience. There is a strong linear relationship between the two variables. The linear regression model has reduced the variability in predicting number of completed interviews by 94.19%. Only 5.81% of the variability in number of completed interviews can be explained by factors other than the weeks of experience.

(g) Coefficient of correlation, $r = \sqrt{r^2}$

$$r = \sqrt{.9419} = .9705$$

Note: r has the same sign (+ or –) as the slope.

(h) Adjusted r^2

$$r_{adj}^2 = 1 - \left[(1 - r^2) \frac{(n - 1)}{(n - 2)} \right]$$

Since $r^2 = .9419$ and $n = 10$:

$$r_{adj}^2 = 1 - \left[(1 - .9419) \frac{(10 - 1)}{(10 - 2)} \right]$$

$$= 1 - [(.0581)(1.125)] = 1 - .0654$$

$$= .9346$$

(i) Hypothesis test for the existence of a relationship between the variables.

H_0: $\beta_1 = 0$ (No relationship)
H_1: $\beta_1 \neq 0$ (Relationship)
$\alpha = .05$

Decision rule:

Reject H_0 if $t_8 >$ 2.3060
        or if $t_8 < -2.3060$
Otherwise, don't reject H_0.

Sample results:

$$b_0 = .173, \quad S_{b_1} = \frac{S_{YX}}{\sqrt{\sum\limits_{i=1}^{n} X_i^2 - \frac{\left(\sum\limits_{i=1}^{n} X_i\right)^2}{n}}} = \frac{.6496}{\sqrt{14141 - \frac{(351)^2}{10}}}$$

$$S_{b_1} = .0152$$

Test statistic:

$$t_8 = \frac{b_1 - \beta_1}{S_{b_1}} = \frac{.173}{.0152} = 11.38$$

Conclusion:

Since $t_8 = 11.38 > 2.3060$, reject H_0. There appears to be a relationship between the variables at $\alpha = .05$.

(j) Confidence interval estimate of average number of interviews completed when $X_i = 20$.

$$\hat{Y}_i \pm t_{n\text{-}2} \, S_{YX} \sqrt{h_i}$$

where $h_i = \dfrac{1}{n} + \dfrac{(X_i - \bar{X})^2}{\sum\limits_{i=1}^{n} X_i^2 - \dfrac{\left(\sum\limits_{i=1}^{n} X_i\right)^2}{n}}$

$\hat{Y}_i = 5.09$ interviews (from d).

$$5.09 \pm 2.306\ (.6496)\ \sqrt{\frac{1}{10} + \frac{(20 - 35.1)^2}{14,141 - \frac{(351)^2}{10}}}$$

$$5.09 \pm 1.498\ \sqrt{.10 + \frac{228.01}{1820.9}}$$

$$5.09 \pm 1.498\ \sqrt{.2252}$$

$$5.09 \pm (1.498)\ (.4746)$$

$$5.09 \pm 0.71$$

$$4.38 \le \mu_{YX} \le 5.80$$

(k) Prediction interval of number of interviews completed when $X_i = 20$ (for an individual interviewer with 20 weeks of experience).

$$\hat{Y}_i \pm t_{n-2}\ S_{YX}\ \sqrt{1 + h_i}$$

where $h_i = \dfrac{1}{n} + \dfrac{(X_i - \bar{X})^2}{\displaystyle\sum_{i=1}^{n} X_i^2 - \dfrac{\left(\displaystyle\sum_{i=1}^{n} X_i\right)^2}{n}}$

$\hat{Y}_i = 1.63 + .173X_i$ and for $X_i = 20$,

$\hat{Y}_i = 5.09$ interviews (see d).

Also $\bar{X} = 35.1$, $S_{YX} = .6496$,

$$\sum_{i=1}^{n} X_i = 351, \sum_{i=1}^{n} X_i^2 = 14{,}141$$

From Table E.3 $t_8 = 2.306$

Thus, $\hat{Y}_i \pm t_{n-2} \; S_{YX} \sqrt{1 + h_i}$

so that $\hat{Y}_i \pm t_{n-2} \; S_{YX} \sqrt{1 + \dfrac{1}{n} + \dfrac{(X_i - \bar{X})^2}{\sum\limits_{i=1}^{n} X_i^2 - \dfrac{\left(\sum\limits_{i=1}^{n} X_i\right)^2}{n}}}$

and $5.09 \pm (2.306)\,(.6496) \sqrt{1 + \dfrac{1}{10} + \dfrac{(20 - 35.1)^2}{14{,}141 - \dfrac{(351)^2}{10}}}$

$5.09 \pm 1.498 \sqrt{1 + .10 + \dfrac{228.01}{1820.9}}$

$5.09 \pm 1.498 \sqrt{1 + .2252}$

$5.09 \pm 1.498 \sqrt{1.2252}$

$5.09 \pm (1.498)\,(1.1069)$

5.09 ± 1.66

Thus, $3.43 \le \hat{Y}_I \le 6.75$

(l) Confidence interval for the true slope.

$\quad b_1 \pm t_{n-2} \; S_{b_1} = .173 \pm 2.306\,(.0152)$

$\qquad\qquad\qquad = .173 \pm .035$

$.138 \le \beta_1 \le .208$

(m) When a regression model is used for prediction purposes, we must only consider the relevant range of the independent variable in making predictions. There is no guarantee that the fitted line will hold outside the range of the observed data.

REVIEW PROBLEM

A limousine service is conducting a study to determine how long it should take to transport passengers from the airport to designated hotels in town. An analyst takes a random sample of 10 recent limousine trips and records the distance in miles and travel time. The table below shows the results:

Trip #	1	2	3	4	5	6	7	8	9	10
Distance (miles)	5.1	6.2	7.5	3.5	4.9	5.5	6.8	6.5	5.4	6.0
Time (minutes)	9.0	10.6	12.9	7.0	8.4	9.4	11.7	11.1	9.3	10.3

(a) Set up a scatter diagram.
(b) Assuming a linear relationship, use the Least Squares method to compute the regression coefficients (b_0 and b_1).
(c) Interpret the meaning of the slope (b_1) in this problem.
(d) If the distance traveled is 5 miles, predict the time it takes.
(e) Compute the standard error of estimate (S_{YX}).
(f) Compute the coefficient of determination (r^2) and interpret its meaning in this problem.
(g) Compute the coefficient of correlation.
(h) Compute the adjusted r^2.
(i) At the .05 level of significance, is there evidence of a relationship between distance traveled and time?
(j) Set up a 95% confidence interval estimate of the average time for all trips for a distance of 5 miles.
(k) Set up a 95% confidence interval estimate of the time of a trip that is 5 miles.
(l) Perform a residual analysis to determine the adequacy of the fit of the model.

SOLUTION TO REVIEW PROBLEM

Basic Computations:

The sums of the following expressions have integer (i) values from 1 to n (n = 10).

$$\sum X_i = 57.4 \qquad \sum X_i^2 = 340.86 \qquad \sum X_i^2 - \frac{\left(\sum X_i\right)^2}{n} = 340.86 - \frac{(57.4)^2}{10}$$

$$= 11.384$$

$$\sum Y_i = 99.7 \qquad \sum Y_i^2 = 1{,}020.37 \qquad \sum Y_i^2 - \frac{\left(\sum Y_i\right)^2}{n} = 1{,}020.37 - \frac{(99.7)^2}{10}$$

$$= 26.361$$

$$\sum X_i Y_i = 589.46 \qquad \sum X_i Y_i - \frac{\left(\sum X_i\right)\left(\sum Y_i\right)}{n} = 589.46 - \frac{(57.4)\,(99.7)}{10}$$

$$= 17.182$$

(a) Scatter diagram of Distance traveled versus Time.

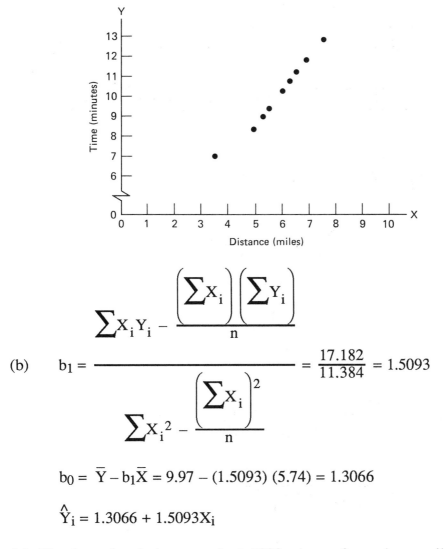

(b) $b_1 = \dfrac{\sum X_i Y_i - \dfrac{\left(\sum X_i\right)\left(\sum Y_i\right)}{n}}{\sum X_i^2 - \dfrac{\left(\sum X_i\right)^2}{n}} = \dfrac{17.182}{11.384} = 1.5093$

$b_0 = \bar{Y} - b_1\bar{X} = 9.97 - (1.5093)(5.74) = 1.3066$

$\hat{Y}_i = 1.3066 + 1.5093 X_i$

(c) The time of a trip increases by 1.5093 minutes for each one mile increase in distance.

(d) If $X_i = 5$, then $\hat{Y}_i = 1.3066 + 1.5093\,(5) = 8.85$ minutes

(e) $S_{YX} = \sqrt{\dfrac{\sum Y_i^2 - b_0 \sum Y_i - b_1 \sum X_i Y_i}{n-2}}$

$= \sqrt{\dfrac{1{,}020.37 - (1.3066)\,(99.7) - (1.5093)\,(589.46)}{10-2}}$

$= \sqrt{\dfrac{.43}{8}} = \sqrt{.05375} = .2318$

(f) $r^2 = 1 - \dfrac{\sum Y_i^2 - b_0 \sum Y_i - b_1 \sum X_i Y_i}{\sum Y_i^2 - \dfrac{\left(\sum Y_i\right)^2}{n}}$

$= 1 - \dfrac{1{,}020.37 - (1.3066)\,(99.7) - (1.5093)\,(589.46)}{1{,}020.37 - \dfrac{(99.7)^2}{10}}$

$= 1 - \dfrac{1{,}020.37 - 130.27 - 889.67}{1{,}020.37 - \dfrac{9{,}940.09}{10}}$

sss $= 1 - \dfrac{.43}{1{,}020.37 - 994.009}$

$= 1 - \dfrac{.43}{26.361}$

$= 1 - .0163$

$= .9837$

(g) $r = \sqrt{r^2} = \sqrt{.9837} = .9918$

(h) $r^2_{adj} = 1 - \left[(1 - r^2) \frac{(n - 1)}{(n - 2)} \right]$

Since $r^2 = .9837$ and $n = 10$

$$r^2_{adj} = 1 - \left[(1 - .9837) \frac{(10 - 1)}{(10 - 2)} \right]$$

$$= 1 - [(.0163) (1.125)]$$

$$= .9817$$

(i) $H_0: \rho = 0$ (No correlation)
    $H_1: \rho \neq 0$ (Correlation)
    $\alpha = .05$

Decision rule:

Reject H_0 if $t_8 > 2.3060$
  or if $t_8 < -2.3060$
Otherwise, do not reject H_0.

Sample result and test statistic:

$$t_8 = \frac{r}{\sqrt{\dfrac{1 - r^2}{n - 2}}} = \frac{.9918}{\sqrt{\dfrac{1 - .9837}{10 - 2}}} = \frac{.9918}{.0451} = 21.99$$

Conclusion:

Since $t_8 = 21.99 > 2.3060$, reject H_0. There appears to be a relationship between the variables at $\alpha = .05$.

(j) $\hat{Y}_i \pm t_{n-2} S_{YX} \sqrt{h_i}$

where $h_i = \dfrac{1}{n} + \dfrac{(X_i - \bar{X})^2}{\displaystyle\sum_{i=1}^{n} X_i^2 - \dfrac{\left(\displaystyle\sum_{i=1}^{n} X_i\right)^2}{n}}$

From (d), if $X_i = 5$, then $\hat{Y}_i = 8.85$ minutes

Thus,

$$8.85 \pm (2.3060)\,(.2318)\,\sqrt{\dfrac{1}{10} + \dfrac{(5 - 5.74)^2}{340.86 - \dfrac{(57.4)^2}{10}}}$$

$$8.85 \pm .5345 \sqrt{\dfrac{1}{10} + \dfrac{.5476}{11.384}}$$

$$8.85 \pm (.5345)\,\sqrt{.1481}$$

$$8.85 \pm (.5345)\,(.3848)$$

$$8.85 \pm .21$$

$$8.64 \le \mu_{YX} \le 9.06$$

(k) $\hat{Y}_i \pm t_{n-2} S_{YX} \sqrt{1 + h_i}$

where $h_i = \dfrac{1}{n} + \dfrac{(X_i - \bar{X})^2}{\displaystyle\sum_{i=1}^{n} X_i^2 - \dfrac{\left(\displaystyle\sum_{i=1}^{n} X_i\right)^2}{n}}$

From (d), if $X_i = 5$, then $\hat{Y}_i = 8.85$ minutes

Also, $\overline{X} = 5.74$, $S_{YX} = .2318$, $\displaystyle\sum_{i=1}^{n} X_i = 57.4$

$$\sum_{i=1}^{n} X_i^2 = 340.86 \qquad \text{From Table E.3} \quad t_8 = 2.3060$$

Thus, $\hat{Y}_i \pm t_{n-2} \, S_{YX} \sqrt{1 + h_i}$

so that

$$\hat{Y}_i \pm t_{n-2} \, S_{YX} \sqrt{1 + \frac{1}{n} \cdot \frac{(X_i - \overline{X})^2}{\displaystyle\sum_{i=1}^{n} X_i^2 - \frac{\left(\displaystyle\sum_{i=1}^{n} X_i\right)^2}{n}}}$$

and

$$8.85 \pm 2.3060 \,(.2318) \sqrt{1 + \frac{1}{10} + \frac{(5 - 5.74)^2}{340.86 - \dfrac{(57.4)^2}{10}}}$$

$$8.85 \pm (.5345) \sqrt{1 + \frac{1}{10} + \frac{(-.74)^2}{340.86 - 329.476}}$$

$$8.85 \pm (.5345) \sqrt{1 + .1481}$$

$$8.85 \pm (.5345) \sqrt{1.1481}$$

$8.85 \pm (.5345) (1.0715)$

$8.85 \pm .57$

Thus, $8.28 \le \hat{Y}_I \le 9.42$

(l) Residual analysis is a graphical approach used to evaluate the adequacy of the fitted model.

Trip #	Distance (X_i)	Time Observed (Y_i)	Predicted $(\hat{Y}_i)$	Residual $(\varepsilon_i = Y_i - \hat{Y}_i)$	h_i	Standardized Residual $\dfrac{\varepsilon_i}{S_{YX}\sqrt{1-h_i}}$
1	5.1	9.0	9.004	−0.004	.1360	−.019
2	6.2	10.6	10.664	−0.064	.1186	−.294
3	7.5	12.9	12.626	0.274	.3721	1.492
4	3.5	7.0	6.589	0.411	.5408	2.616
5	4.9	8.4	8.702	−0.302	.1620	−1.423
6	5.5	9.4	9.608	−0.208	.1051	−.948
7	6.8	11.7	11.570	0.130	.1987	.627
8	6.5	11.1	11.117	−0.017	.1507	−.080
9	5.4	9.3	9.457	−0.157	.1102	−.718
10	6.0	10.3	10.362	−0.062	.1059	−.283

$\hat{Y}_i = 1.3066 + 1.5093 \, X_i$ $\qquad\qquad \bar{X} = 5.74$

$S_{YX} = .2318$ $\qquad\qquad h_i = \dfrac{1}{n} + \dfrac{(X_i - \bar{X})^2}{\displaystyle\sum_{i=1}^{n} X_i^2 - \dfrac{\left(\displaystyle\sum_{i=1}^{n} X_i\right)^2}{n}}$

Scatter plot of standardized residuals versus distance (in miles).

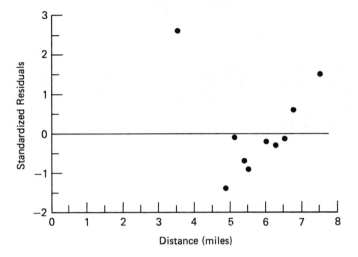

The standardized residuals have been plotted against the independent variable (distance). From this graph we observe that one point ($X_i = 3.5$, $\varepsilon_i = 2.616$) has a large residual and may be influencing the model since $X_i = 3.5$ is substantially below the other X_i values. Disregarding this point there appears to be a trend in the residuals. Thus, we might wish to consider a model where $X_i = 3.5$ is deleted and analyze a smaller range of X values.

17

Multiple Regression Models

In our discussion of regression and correlation we have focused upon a linear relationship between one independent variable and a dependent variable. The basic concepts of regression and correlation can be extended to a multiple regression model that involves several independent variables. In multiple regression, not only can we determine the relationship of the set of independent variables with a dependent variable, but we can assess the contribution of each independent variable to the model. In this manner, we can determine which of several alternative models is most appropriate from the point of view of both simplicity and goodness of fit. In addition to the evaluation of several independent variables, we may also wish to fit relationships that are not linear between an independent and dependent variable. Moreover, we may wish to use dummy variables in order to develop multiple regression models in which at least one of the independent variables is qualitative. The chapter concludes with an example of model building through stepwise regression using computer packages.

MULTIPLE CHOICE

1. In determining whether there is a significant relationship between the dependent variable and the set of independent variables, one may use an F test, where the _____ is divided by the _____.

     a. total variance; error variance
     b. variance due to regression; total variance
     c. error variance; variance due to regression
     d. variance due to regression; error variance

2. The error variance is also

     a. the total sum of squares minus the sum of squares due to regression.
     b. the square of the standard error of the estimate.
     c. the square root of the coefficient of multiple determination.
     d. the reciprocal of the total variance.

3. If a sample has 18 observations and two explanatory variables, then the critical value of F at a .05 level of significance is

     a. 3.55.
     b. 3.68.
     c. 19.43.
     d. 19.45.

4. The partial F test criterion is used

     a. to determine whether there is a significant relationship between the dependent variable and the set of explanatory variables.
     b. for determining the contribution of an explanatory variable.
     c. to test for independence of error.
     d. to test for multicollinearity.

5. Which of the following may be used to determine the contribution of an explanatory variable?

    a. the partial F test criterion

    b. use of the standard error of a regression coefficient so that

$$\frac{\left(b_k^2 \ S_{YX}^2 \right)}{S_{b_k}^2}$$

    c. VIF

    d. a and b

6. The t test for the regression coefficient is equivalent to

    a. testing for interaction effects in a regression model.

    b. testing for the contribution of each explanatory variable (i.e., $t_a^2 = F_{1,a}$, where a = number of degrees of freedom).

    c. testing for multicollinearity.

    d. testing for the contribution of the curvilinear effect to a regression model.

7. A measure of the proportion of the variation in the dependent variable that is explained by each explanatory variable while controlling for the other explanatory variable(s) is called

    a. the coefficient of multiple determination.

    b. the coefficient of partial determination.

    c. the net regression coefficient.

    d. the multiple correlation coefficient.

8. Centering the curvilinear regression model is often recommended because

    a. it may explain more of the total variation than an uncentered model.

    b. it may be easier to interpret the value of b_{11}.

    c. it may reduce problems of multicollinearity present in an uncentered model.

    d. a and b.

9. Dummy variables are used in regression analysis when the researcher wants to

    a. straighten out a curvilinear relationship.
    b. include qualitative explanatory variables in the model.
    c. include quantitative discrete data in the model.
    d. test for the contribution of particular explanatory variables.

EXAMPLES

I. An investment firm would like to develop a model to predict the revenue generated by a broker in a given time period on the basis of age of broker and years of experience. A random sample of 10 brokers is selected with the following results:

Broker #	Revenue (in thousands) (Y_i)	Age (in years) (X_{1i})	Years of Experience (X_{2i})
1	52	30	2
2	67	27	4
3	43	32	3
4	64	26	3
5	58	34	5
6	69	29	4
7	73	28	5
8	46	30	3
9	55	32	4
10	75	26	4

(a) Assuming that each independent variable (age and years of experience) is linearly related to revenue, use the least squares method to find the multiple regression coefficients (b_0, b_1, b_2).
(b) Interpret the meaning of the slopes in this example.
(c) Predict the revenue when age is 31 and years of experience is 4.5.

(d) Determine whether there is a significant relationship between revenue and the two independent variables (age and years of experience) at the .01 level of significance.

(e) Compute the standard error of the estimate (S_{YX}), the coefficient of multiple determination ($r^2_{Y.12}$), the adjusted R^2_{adj}, and the coefficient of correlation ($R_{Y.12}$). Interpret the meaning of $r^2_{Y.12}$ and R^2_{adj} in this example.

(f) At the .01 level of significance, determine whether each independent variable makes a contribution to the regression model. Based upon the results, indicate the regression model that should be used in this example.

(g) Compute the coefficients of partial determination ($r^2_{Y1.2}$) and ($r^2_{Y2.1}$) and interpret their meaning in this example.

(h) Is there any reason to "suspect" any multicollinearity in the data? Explain.

SOLUTION

Parts of this example will be solved by SPSS[X].

(a)

```
------------------ VARIABLES IN THE EQUATION ------------------
```

VARIABLE		B		SE B	T	SIG T
X_1 = AGE	b_1 =	-3.003377	S_{b_1} =	.581957	-5.161	.0013
X_2 = EXPER	b_2 =	7.556473	S_{b_2} =	1.666221	4.535	.0027
(CONSTANT)	b_0 =	120.540338	S_{b_0} =	17.690680	6.814	.0003

(b) The slope of age with revenue generated (b_1), computed as -3.003377, can be interpreted to mean that for a given number of years of experience, the revenue generated will decrease $3,003.38 for each one year increase in age. Furthermore, the slope of the number of years of experience with revenue generated (b_2), computed as 7.556473, can be interpreted to mean that for a given age, the revenue generated will increase $7,556.47 for each one year increase in experience.

(c) For $X_1 = 31$ (age in years) and $X_2 = 4.3$ (years of experience),

$$\hat{Y}_i = 120.540338 - 3.003377X_{1i} + 7.556473X_{2i}$$

$$= 120.540338 - 3.003377\,(31) + 7.556473\,(4.5)$$

$$= 61.4397795 \text{ thousands of dollars}$$

(d) H_0: $\beta_1 = \beta_2 = 0$ (There is no relationship between revenue generated and age and years of experience.)

H_1: $\beta_1 \neq \beta_2 \neq 0$ (At least one regression coefficient is not equal to zero.)

$\alpha = .01$

Decision rule:

Reject H_0 if $F_{2,7} > 9.55$
Otherwise, don't reject H_0.

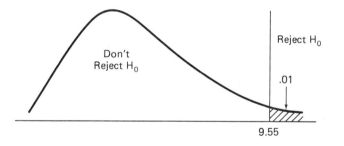

Sample results and test statistic:

```
ANALYSIS OF VARIANCE
                    DF              SUM OF SQUARES       MEAN SQUARE
REGRESSION           2    SSR(b₁ & b₂) = 961.60075        480.80038
RESIDUAL             7                    155.99925        22.28561


F =        21.57448          SIGNIF F =   .0010
```

Conclusion:

Since $F_{2,7} = 21.57448 > 9.55$, reject H_0. The investment firm may conclude that at least one of the independent variables (age and/or years of experience) is related to revenue generated at the .01 level of significance.

(e)

MULTIPLE R	$r_{Y.12} =$	.92759
R SQUARE	$r^2_{Y.12} =$	.86042
ADJUSTED R SQUARE		.82053
STANDARD ERROR	$s_{YX} =$	4.72076

$$r^2_{adj} = 1 - \left[(1 - r^2) \; \frac{(n - 1)}{(n - p - 1)} \right]$$

where p is the number of explanatory variables in the regression equation. Thus, for our data, since $r^2 = .86042$, $n = 10$, and $p = 2$,

$$r^2_{adj} = 1 - \left[(1 - .86042) \; \frac{(10 - 1)}{(10 - 2 - 1)} \right]$$

$$= 1 - [(.13958)(1.2857143)]$$

$$= .82053$$

In this example 86.04% of the variation in revenue generated can be explained by age and years of experience.

82.05% of the variation in revenue generated can be explained by our multiple regression model adjusted for number of predictors and sample size.

(f) (1) Contribution of X_1.

H_0: Age (X_1) does not significantly improve the model once years of experience (X_2) has already been included (i.e., $\beta_1 = 0$).

H_1: Age significantly improves the model once years of experience has already been included (i.e., $\beta_1 \neq 0$).

$\alpha = .01$

Decision rule:

Reject H_0 if $t_7 < -3.4995$
   or if $t_7 > 3.4995$
Otherwise, don't reject H_0.

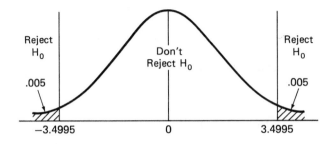

Sample results and test statistic:

```
------------------- VARIABLES IN THE EQUATION -------------------
```

VARIABLE		B		SE B	T	SIG T
X_1 = AGE	b_1 =	-3.003377	S_{b_1} =	.581957	-5.161	.0013
X_2 = EXPER	b_2 =	7.556473	S_{b_2} =	1.666221	4.535	.0027
(CONSTANT)	b_0 =	120.540338	S_{b_0} =	17.690680	6.814	.0003

$$\textit{Note: } t_{n-p-1} = \frac{b_1 - \beta_1}{S_{b_1}} = \frac{-3.003377}{.581957} = -5.161$$

Conclusion:

Since the computed $t = -5.161 < -3.4995$, reject H_0. The addition of age significantly improves the multiple regression model that already contains years of experience.

(2) Contribution of X_2.

H_0:   Years of experience does not significantly improve the model once age has already been included (i.e., $\beta_2 = 0$).

H_1:   Years of experience significantly improves the model once age has already been included (i.e., $\beta_2 \neq 0$).

$\alpha = .01$

Decision rule:

   Same as in (f.1).

Sample results and test statistic:

Note: $t_{n-p-1} = \dfrac{b_2 - \beta_2}{S_{b_2}} = \dfrac{7.556473}{1.666221} = 4.535$

[See printout in part (f.1)].

Conclusion:

   Since $t = 4.535 > 3.4995$, reject H_0. The addition of years of experience significantly improves the multiple regression model that already contains age.

   The multiple regression model should include both age and years of experience, since the contribution of each of the two independent variables after the other was already included in the model was significant.

(g) $SSR(X_1|X_2) = \dfrac{b_1^2 \, S_{YX}^2}{S_{b_1}^2} = \dfrac{(-3.003377)^2 \, (4.72076)^2}{(.581957)^2} = 593.55607$

$SSR(X_2|X_1) = \dfrac{b_2^2 \, S_{YX}^2}{S_{b_2}^2} = \dfrac{(7.556473)^2 \, (4.72076)^2}{(1.666221)^2} = 458.34965$

$SST = 961.60075 + 155.99925 = 1{,}117.6$

   [from printout part (d)].

$$r^2_{Y1.2} = \frac{SSR(X_1|X_2)}{SST - SSR\ (X_1\ and\ X_2) + SSR\ (X_1|X_2)}$$

$$= \frac{593.55607}{1,117.6 - 961.60075 + 593.55607}$$

$$= .79188$$

$$r^2_{Y2.1} = \frac{SSR(X_2|X_1)}{SST - SSR\ (X_1\ and\ X_2) + SSR\ (X_2|X_1)}$$

$$= \frac{458.34965}{1,117.6 - 961.60075 + 458.34965}$$

$$= \frac{458.34965}{614.3489}$$

$$= .74607$$

The coefficient of partial determination of revenue generated with age while holding years of experience constant $(r^2_{Y1.2})$ may be interpreted to mean that for a fixed number of years of experience, 79.19% of the variation in revenue generated is explained by age. Furthermore, the coefficient of partial determination of revenue generated with years of experience while holding age constant $(r^2_{Y2.1})$ may be interpreted to mean that for a fixed age, 74.61% of the variation in revenue generated is explained by years of experience.

(h) We measure for collinearity using the variance inflationary factor (VIF) which can be obtained as output from various computer packages.

$$VIF_j = \frac{1}{1 - R^2_j}$$

where R^2_j represents the coefficient of multiple determination of explanatory variable j with all other X variables. (Remember that when there are only two explanatory variables, R^2_j is simply the coefficient of determination between X_1 and X_2.)

$$VIF_1 = VIF_2 = \frac{1}{1 - (-.09486)^2}$$

$$VIF_1 = VIF_2 \cong 1$$

As a rule of thumb, if $VIF_j > 10$, there is too much correlation between variable X_j and the other explanatory variables. Therefore, we may conclude that there is no reason to suspect any multicollinearity between age and years of experience.

II. A bank would like to develop a model to predict the total sum of money that customers withdraw from ATMs on a weekend based on the location of the ATM (0 = a shopping center and 1 = not a shopping center) and the median value of homes in the neighborhood where the ATM is located. A random sample of 15 ATMs is selected with the following results:

ATM #	Total Money Withdrawn (in thousands) (Y_i)	Median Value of Homes (in thousands) (X_{1i})	Location of ATM (X_{2i})
1	120	225	0
2	99	170	1
3	91	153	0
4	82	132	1
5	124	237	0
6	104	187	0
7	127	245	0
8	80	125	0
9	115	215	0
10	97	170	1
11	117	223	1
12	86	147	1
13	109	197	0
14	94	167	1
15	112	210	1

Use a computer package to perform a multiple linear regression analysis.

(a) Based upon the results obtained, state the multiple regression equation.
(b) Interpret the meaning of the slopes in this example.
(c) Predict the total money withdrawn on a weekend for a neighborhood where the median value of homes is $150,000 and the ATM is not located in a shopping center.
(d) Is there evidence of a relationship between the total sum of money withdrawn on a weekend and the two independent variables (median value of homes and location) at the .05 level of significance? Find the p-value.
(e) Interpret the meaning of the coefficient of multiple determination $r^2_{Y.12}$.
(f) At the .05 level of significance determine whether each independent variable makes a contribution to the regression model. Based upon these results, indicate the regression model that should be utilized in this example.
(g) Set up a 95% confidence interval estimate of the average amount of money withdrawn when the median home value is 187 (in thousands) and the ATM is located in a shopping center.
(h) Set up a 95% confidence interval estimate of the true population slope between amount of money withdrawn and median home value.
(i) Compute the coefficients of partial determination ($r^2_{Y1.2}$ and $r^2_{Y2.1}$) and interpret their meaning in this problem.

SOLUTION

(a)

PARAMETER	ESTIMATE	T FOR HO: PARAMETER=0	STD ERROR OF ESTIMATE
INTERCEPT	b_0=30.91053884	20.65	S_{b_0}= 1.49669855
X_1=HOMEVALU	b_1= 0.39312859	53.52	S_{b_1}= 0.00734560
X_2=ATM	b_2=-1.22821788	-2.25	S_{b_2}= 0.54590927

Assuming that the slope between amount of money withdrawn and median home value is the same for both locations, the regression model could be stated as:

$$\hat{Y}_i = 30.91053884 + .39312859X_{1_i} - 1.22821788X_{2_i}$$

(b) The slope of the median value of homes with the amount of money withdrawn (b_1), computed as .39312859, can be interpreted to mean that when the effect of ATM location is held constant, the total money withdrawn will increase by $393.13 for each additional $1,000 in median value of homes. The slope of location (b_2) measures the effect of total money withdrawn from an ATM located in a shopping center ($X_2 = 0$) as compared to an ATM not located in a shopping center ($X_2 = 1$). Thus, when the median value of homes is held constant, the average amount of money withdrawn from an ATM not located in a shopping center is $1,228.22 lower than that withdrawn from an ATM located in a shopping center.

(c) Prediction of the dependent variable, $\hat{Y}_i$, for given values of the independent variables.

$$\hat{Y}_i = 30.91053884 + .39312859X_{1i} - 1.22821788X_{2i}$$

For $X_1 = 150$ (thousands of dollars) and $X_2 = 0$ (located in a shopping center)

$$\hat{Y}_i = 30.91053884 + .39312859 \,(150) - 1.22821788 \,(0)$$

$$= 89.879827 \text{ thousands of dollars withdrawn}$$

(d) Hypothesis test for the relationship between the dependent and the independent variables:

H_0: $\beta_1 = \beta_2 = 0$ (There is no relationship between total money withdrawn and the median home value and ATM location.)

H_1: $\beta_1 \neq \beta_2 \neq 0$ (At least one regression coefficient is not equal to zero.)

$\alpha = .05$

Decision rule:

Reject H_0 if $F_{2,12} > 3.89$
Otherwise, don't reject H_0.

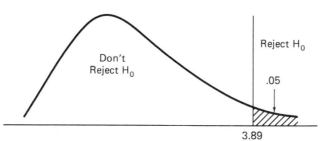

Sample results and test statistic:

ANALYSIS OF VARIANCE TABLE FOR TESTING
THE SIGNFICANCE OF TWO REGRESSION COEFFICIENTS

SOURCE	DF	SUM OF SQUARES	MEAN SQUARE	F VALUE
MODEL	2	SSR(X_1 and X_2) = 3278.42468640	1639.21234320	1642.59
ERROR	12	11.97531360	$S_{YX}^2 = 0.99794280$	
				PR > F
CORRECTED TOTAL	14	3290.40000000		0.0001

Conclusion:

Since $F = 1,642.59 > 3.89$, reject H_0. The bank may conclude that at least one of the independent variables (median home value and/or ATM location) is related to the total money withdrawn at the .05 level of significance.

The p-value for this example is .0001.

(e)

$$R-SQUARE$$

$$r_{Y.12}^2 = 0.996361$$

In this example, 99.64% of the variation in total money withdrawn is explained by median value of homes and ATM location.

(f) Determination of the contribution of each independent variable.

(1) Contribution of X_1.

H_0: Median home value (X_1) does not significantly improve the model once ATM location (X_2) has already been included (i.e., $\beta_1 = 0$).

H_1: Median home value significantly improves the model once ATM location has already been included (i.e., $\beta_1 \neq 0$).

$\alpha = .05$

Decision rule:

Reject H_0 if $F_{1,12} > 4.75$
Otherwise, don't reject H_0.

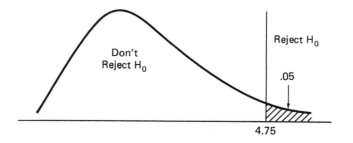

Sample results and test statistic:

SOURCE	DF	TYPE III SS	F VALUE
X_1 = HOMEVALU	1	SSR(X_1|X_2)=2858.38182926	2864.27
X_2 = ATM	1	SSR(X_2|X_1)= 5.05144394	5.06

$$F_{1,12} = \frac{SSR\ (X_1|X_2)}{MSE} = \frac{2858.38182926}{.99794280} = 2,864.27$$

(*Note:* Since $t_{n-3}^2 = F_{1,n-3}$, an equivalent test for the contribution of each independent variable would be the t test for the regression coefficient:

$$\text{i.e., } t = \frac{b_1 - \beta_1}{S_{b_1}} = \frac{.39312859}{.00734560} = 53.52$$

[See printout part (a).]

Conclusion:

Since the computed F = 2864.27 > 4.75, reject H_0. (Similarly, since t = 53.52 > 2.1788, reject H_0. The addition of variable X_1 (median home value) significantly improves the multiple regression model that already contains variable X_2 (ATM location).

(2) Contribution of X_2.

H_0: ATM location does not significantly improve the model once median home value has already been included (i.e., $\beta_2 = 0$).

H_1: ATM location significantly improves the model one median home value has already been included (i.e., $\beta_2 \neq 0$).

$\alpha = .05$

Decision rule:

Same as in (f.1).

Sample results and test statistic:

$$F_{1,12} = \frac{\text{SSR } (X_2|X_1)}{\text{MSE}} = \frac{5.05144394}{.99794280} = 5.06$$

[See printout in (f.1).]

Conclusion:

> Since the computed $F = 5.06 > 4.75$, reject H_0. The addition of variable X_2 (ATM location) significantly improves the multiple regression model that already contains variable X_1 (median home value).
>
> The multiple regression model should include both median home value and ATM location in predicting total money withdrawn on a weekend since the contribution of each of the two independent variables after the other was already included in the model was significant.

(g) Confidence interval estimates for predicting μ_{YX} are given for each observation in the sample by the SAS GLM procedure.

OBSERVATION	PREDICTED VALUE	LOWER 95% CL FOR MEAN	UPPER 95% CL FOR MEAN
1	119.36447198	118.48190859	120.24703536
2	96.51418155	95.68884629	97.33951681
3	91.05921337	90.00522588	92.11320086
4	81.57529506	80.51147598	82.63911414
5	124.08201508	123.09116211	125.07286804
6	104.42558549	103.63616899	105.21500199
7	127.22704381	126.15092979	128.30315783
8	80.05161280	78.65260886	81.45061674
9	115.43318606	114.61696810	116.24940402
10	96.51418155	95.68884629	97.33951681
11	117.34999691	116.21499947	118.48499436
12	87.47222394	86.54190296	88.40254491
13	108.35687141	107.58716996	109.12657285
14	95.33479577	94.50422319	96.16536836
15	112.23932522	111.23626793	113.24238251

The 95% confidence interval estimate of the average total money withdrawn (in thousands) when the median home value $X_1 = 187$ (in thousands) and the ATM is located in a shopping center $X_2 = 0$ is:

$$103.63616899 \leq \mu_{YX} \leq 105.21500199$$

(h) Confidence interval estimate for β_1: $(b_1 \pm t_{n-p-1} S_{b_1})$

   $.39312859 \pm (2.1788) (.00734560) =$

   $.39312859 \pm .01600459$

   $.37712400 \leq \beta_1 \leq .40913318$

(i) Coefficient of Partial Determination.

$$r^2_{Y1.2} = \frac{SSR\ (X_1|X_2)}{SST - SSR\ (X_1\ and\ X_2) + SSR\ (X_1|X_2)}$$

and

$$r^2_{Y2.1} = \frac{SSR\ (X_2|X_1)}{SST - SSR\ (X_1\ and\ X_2) + SSR\ (X_2|X_1)}$$

where

   SSR $(X_1|X_2)$ = Sum of squares of the contribution of variable X_1 to the regression model given that variable X_2 is already included in the model
   = 2858.38182926 [from printout in part (f): Type III SS].

   SST = Total sum of squares for Y
   = SSR $(X_1$ and $X_2)$ + SSE
   = 3278.42468640 + 11.97531360
   = 3290.40000000 [from printout in part (d)].

   SSR $(X_1$ and $X_2)$ = Regression sum of squares when variables X_1 and X_2 are both included in the multiple regression model = 3278.42468640 [from printout in part (d)].

$$\text{SSR } (X_2|X_1) = \text{Sum of squares of the contribution of variable } X_2 \text{ to the regression model given that variable } X_1 \text{ is already included in the model} = 5.05144394 \text{ [from printout in part (f): Type III SS].}$$

$$r_{Y1.2}^2 = \frac{2858.38182926}{3290.400 - 3278.42468640 + 2858.38182926}$$

$$= \frac{2858.3812926}{2870.35714286} = .99583$$

$$r_{Y2.1}^2 = \frac{5.05144394}{3290.4000 - 3278.42468640 + 5.05144394}$$

$$= \frac{5.05144394}{17.02675754} = .29668$$

The coefficient of partial determination of variable total money withdrawn (Y) with median home value (X_1) while holding ATM location (X_2) constant ($r_{Y1.2}^2$) can be interpreted to mean that for a fixed ATM location, 99.58% of the variation in total money withdrawn can be explained by the variation in median home value. Similarly, the coefficient of partial determination of total money withdrawn (Y) with ATM location (X_2) while holding median home value (X_1) constant ($r_{Y2.1}^2$) can be interpreted to mean that for a fixed median home value, 29.67% of the variation in total money withdrawn can be explained by variation in ATM location.

III. A conductor of an orchestra wants to develop a model to predict the number of mistakes made by musicians during a two hour performance on the basis of the number of hours that were spent practicing before a concert. The conductor gathered the following data from 10 musicians in the orchestra:

Musician	Hours Spent Practicing X	Number of Errors Y
1	0.0	11
2	2.0	9
3	4.0	7
4	6.0	4
5	8.0	3
6	10.0	2
7	12.0	5
8	14.0	6
9	16.0	8
10	18.0	10

Calculate the curvilinear regression equation using the centering method.

SOLUTION

Parts of this example will be solved using SPSS[X].

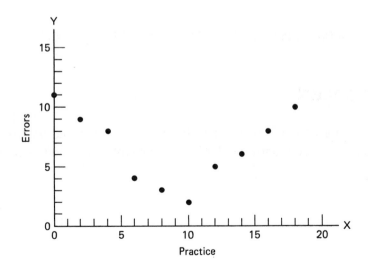

Scattergram of "Errors" with "Practice"

Calculating the curvilinear regression equation using the centering method:

$$\hat{Y}_i = b_0' + b_1' (X_{1_i} - \overline{X}) + b_{11}' (X_{1_i} - \overline{X})^2$$

```
------------------ VARIABLES IN THE EQUATION ------------------
```

VARIABLE		B	SE B	BETA	T	SIG T
X_2= PRACSOU	b_{11}'=	.094697	.009773	.958266	9.689	.0000
X_1= PRAC	b_1'=	-.057576	.049449	-.115152	-1.164	.2824
(CONSTANT)	b_0'=	3.375000	.429780		7.853	.0001

MULTIPLE R	.96516
R SQUARE	.93153
ADJUSTED R SQUARE	.91197
STANDARD ERROR	.89829

The regression equation is:

$$\hat{Y}_i = 3.375000 - .057576 (X_{1_i} - \overline{X}) + .094697 (X_{1_i} - \overline{X})^2$$

REVIEW PROBLEM

A pool supply company would like to predict weekly sales based on temperature and inches of rainfall. A random sample of 10 time periods is selected with the following results:

Time Period #	Sales (in thousands) (Y)	Inches of Rainfall (X$_1$)	Temperature $^\circ$F (X$_2$)
1	16	3.00	75
2	21	2.75	85
3	23	2.75	91
4	20	2.50	82
5	17	3.00	77
6	24	2.75	92
7	22	2.25	89
8	21	2.75	87
9	26	1.75	93
10	18	2.75	79

(a) Assuming that each independent variable (temperature and inches of rainfall) is linearly related to sales, use the least squares method to find the multiple regression coefficients.

(b) Interpret the meaning of the slopes in this example.

(c) Predict the sales when the temperature is 80°F and the rainfall is 1.75 inches.

(d) Determine whether there is significant relationship between sales and the two independent variables (temperature and inches of rainfall) at the .05 level of significance. Find the p-value for this problem.

(e) Interpret the meaning of the coefficient of multiple determination ($r^2_{Y.12}$) as well as the adjusted r^2 in this problem.

(f) At the .05 level of significance, determine whether each independent variable makes a contribution to the regression model. Based upon these results, indicate the regression model that should be used in this example.

SOLUTION

Parts of this example will be solved using SPSS^X.

```
------------------ VARIABLES IN THE EQUATION ------------------

VARIABLE                  B              SE B          T       SIG T

X₁ = RAIN   b₁ =   -1.539373   Sᵦ₁ =  .610046    -2.523    .0396
X₂ = TEMP   b₂ =     .420195   Sᵦ₂ =  .035517    11.831    .0000
(CONSTANT)  b₀ = -10.875699    Sᵦ₀ = 4.212894    -2.582    .0364
```

(b) The slope of rain with sales (b_1), computed as -1.539373, can be interpreted to mean that for a given temperature, the sales will decrease $1,539.37 for each one inch of rainfall. Furthermore, the slope of temperature with sales (b_2), computed as .420195, can be interpreted to mean that for a given amount of rainfall, the sales will increase $420.20 for each one degree increase in temperature.

(c) For $X_1 = 1.75$ (inches of rainfall) and $X_2 = 80$ (degrees F)

$$\hat{Y}_i = -10.875699 - 1.539373 X_{1i} + .420195 X_{2i}$$

$$= -10.875699 - 1.539373 (1.75) + .420195 (80)$$

$$= 20.045998 \text{ thousands of dollars}$$

(d) H_0: $\beta_1 = \beta_2 = 0$ (There is no relationship between sales and the temperature and inches of rainfall.)

    H_1: $\beta_1 \neq \beta_2 \neq 0$ (At least one regression coefficient is not equal to zero.)

    $\alpha = .05$

Decision rule:

       Reject H_0 if $F_{2,7} > 4.74$
       Otherwise, don't reject H_0.

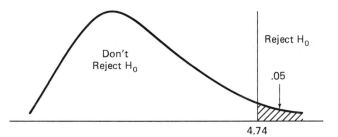

4.74

Sample results and test statistic:

```
ANALYSIS OF VARIANCE
                    DF              SUM OF SQUARES        MEAN SQUARE
REGRESSION           2    SSR(X₁ & X₂) = 87.56520         43.78260
RESIDUAL             7                    2.03480           .29069

F =    150.61826        SIGNIF F =   .0000
```

Conclusion:

Since $F_{2,7} = 150.61826 > 4.74$, reject H_0. The pool company may conclude that at least one of the independent variables (rainfall) and/or temperature) is related to sales at the .05 level of significance.

(e)

```
MULTIPLE R           r_{y.12}  = .98858
R SQUARE             r²_{Y.12} = .97729

ADJUSTED R SQUARE    r²_{adj}  = .97080

STANDARD ERROR       S_{YX}    = .53915
```

$$r^2_{adj} = 1 - \left[(1 - r^2) \frac{(n-1)}{(n-p-1)} \right]$$

where p is the number of explanatory variables in the regression equation. Thus, for our data, since $r^2 = .97729$, n = 10, and p = 2.

$$r_{adj}^2 = 1 - \left[(1 - .97729) \; \frac{(10 - 1)}{(10 - 2 - 1)} \right]$$

$$= 1 - \left[(.02271) \; \frac{9}{7} \right]$$

$$= 1 - [(.02271) (1.2857142)]$$

$$= .9708014$$

In this example 97.73% of the variation in sales can be explained by rainfall and temperature.

97.08% of the variation in sales can be explained by our multiple regression model adjusted for number of predictors and sample size.

(f) (1) Contribution of X_1.

H_0: Rainfall (X_1) does not significantly improve the model once temperature (X_2) has already been included (i.e., $\beta_1 = 0$).

H_1: Rainfall significantly improves the model once temperature has already been included (i.e., $\beta_1 \neq 0$).

$\alpha = .05$

Decision rule:

Reject H_0 if $t_7 < -2.3646$
or if $t_7 > 2.3646$
Otherwise, don't reject H_0.

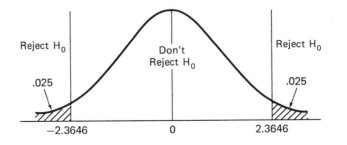

From part (a) of the solution:

$$t = \frac{b_1 - \beta_1}{S_{b_1}} = \frac{-1.539373 - 0}{.610046} = -2.523$$

Conclusion:

Since the computed $t = -2.523 < 2.3646$, reject H_0. The addition of rainfall significantly improves the multiple regression model that already contains temperature.

(2) Contribution of X_2.

        H_0:   Temperature does not significantly improve the model once rainfall has already been included (i.e., $\beta_2 = 0$).

        H_1:   Temperature significantly improves the model once rainfall has already been included (i.e., $\beta_2 \neq 0$).

Decision rule:

Same as in (f.1).

Sample results and test statistic:

$$\textit{Note:} \quad t = \frac{b_2 - \beta_2}{S_{b_2}} = \frac{.420195 - 0}{.035517} = 11.831$$

Conclusion:

Since $t = 11.831 > 2.523$, reject H_0. The addition of temperature significantly improves the multiple regression model that already contains rainfall. The multiple regression model should include both rainfall and temperature in predicting sales, since the contribution of each of the two independent variables after the other was already included in the model was significant.

18

Index Numbers, Time Series, and Business Forecasting

Over the years index numbers have become increasingly important to business and government leaders as indicators of changing economic or business activity. In fact, the use of index numbers has become the most widely accepted procedure for measuring changes in business conditions. Thus, the first part of this chapter focuses upon the concepts of index number construction. In particular, the development and use of various price indexes are considered and the importance of the well-known Consumer Price Index is described. In addition, such concepts as aggregate price indexes versus mean price relatives, nominal versus real wages, and index number adjustments are discussed.

The second part of this chapter focuses on time series analysis. Since economic and business conditions vary over time, business leaders must find ways to keep abreast of the effects that such changes will have on their particular operations. One such method which business leaders may use as an aid in controlling present operations and in planning for future needs (by forecasting likely developments in sales, raw materials, etc.) is time-series analysis. The basic assumption of classical time-series analysis is that those factors which have influenced patterns of economic activity in the past and present will continue to do so in more or less the same manner in the future. Thus, the major goals of time-series analysis are to isolate these influencing factors for forecasting purposes as well as for managerial planning and control. The classical multiplicative time-series model, which has been used for exploring the fluctuations among the component factors of a series in order to achieve the aforementioned goals, is developed. Such concepts as time-series decomposition, moving averages, exponential smoothing, and seasonal index utilization are discussed. In addition, the concept of MAD is introduced as a measure of the forecasting error when comparing linear, quadratic, exponential, and other forecasting models.

MULTIPLE CHOICE

1. The reference point against which all index numbers are computed is called

     a. the price relative.
     b. the commodity list.
     c. the base period.
     d. the aggregate value.

2. An aggregate price index represents

     a. the changes in prices, over time, for an entire group of commodities.
     b. the average of the changes in prices, over time, of each commodity in the index.
     c. only perishable commodities.
     d. None of the above.

3. In a "fixed" weight index the weights may be

     a. established at a particular point in time.
     b. developed as an average over several periods of time.
     c. Neither of the above.
     d. Both of the above.

4. The *new* Consumer Price Index for All Urban Consumers includes persons

   a. living in institutions.
   b. who are unemployed.
   c. in the military service.
   d. living on farms.

5. To use the CPI as a "deflator" of nominal wages:

   a. Real Wages = (Nominal Wages ÷ CPI) x 100.
   b. Real Wages = (Nominal Wages x CPI) ÷ 100.
   c. Real Wages = (Nominal Wages + CPI) – 100.
   d. Real Wages = (Nominal Wages – CPI) + 100.

6. In the decomposition of monthly time series data, the component which remains after all others are eliminated is

   a. the irregular movement.
   b. the cyclical effect.
   c. the seasonal variation.
   d. the trend.

7. The method of least squares is used on time-series data for

   a. eliminating irregular movements.
   b. deseasonalizing the data.
   c. obtaining the trend equation.
   d. exponentially smoothing a series.

8. Erratic, unsystematic fluctuations in a time series which are caused by such special unpredictable events as assassinations, floods, strikes, wars, etc. are called

   a. seasonal variations.
   b. cyclical fluctuations.
   c. secular trends.
   d. irregular movements.

9. The persistent or overall tendency in a time series is called

    a. exponential smoothing.
    b. a moving average.
    c. irregular movements.
    d. the trend.

10. The annual multiplicative time series model does not possess a _____ component.

    a. irregular
    b. cyclical
    c. trend
    d. seasonal

11. Which of the following statements about the seasonal index in a time series are true?

    a. It can be used to adjust a trend projection.
    b. It can be used to help evaluate a particular month's results against previous results.
    c. It can be used to eliminate the seasonal factors in the series.
    d. All of the above.

12. Which of the following statements about the method of exponential smoothing is *not* true?

    a. It gives greater weight to more recent data.
    b. It can be used for forecasting trend.
    c. It can be used in lieu of moving averages to smooth a series.
    d. It gives greater weight to past data.

EXAMPLES

I. The following table presents the median salary schedules (in thousands of dollars) for the full-time instructional staff of a large, well-known university:

Position	Number* and Pay**	Year		
		1972	1976	1980
Professor	Q	111	100	92
	P	22.0	24.2	26.7
Associate Professor	Q	325	309	301
	P	17.5	19.7	22.3
Assistant Professor	Q	328	341	386
	P	12.2	14.9	18.3
Instructor	Q	232	221	197
	P	10.9	12.7	16.1

*Q = Number of employees.
**P = Median pay per annum in thousands of dollars.

Moreover, the following table presents the Consumer Price Index compiled for the particular geographic region in which the university is located:

	Year		
Consumer Price Index (1967 = 100.0)	1972	1976	1980
	118.1	145.2	197.5

(a) Using 1972 as the "base pay" year, construct the following indexes of salaries paid to the full-time instructional staff at this university for the year 1980:
   (1) Simple Aggregate Index.
   (2) "Fixed" Weights Aggregate Index (using 1976 as the weight period).

  (b) Determine the percentage growth rate in "nominal" salaries paid to assistant professors over the 8-year period 1972 to 1980.

  (c) Deflate the 1972 and 1980 figures by the Consumer Price Index for those years.

  (d) Determine the percentage growth rate in "real" salaries paid to assistant professors over the 8-year period 1972 to 1980.

  (e) Discuss how the purchasing power of assistant professors at this university has changed from 1972 to 1980.

SOLUTION

  (a) Let the base year period 1972 be given the code 0. The index in the base year period is 100.0.

      Let 1976 be given the code 1.

      Let 1980 be given the code 2.

      (1) Simple Aggregate Index.

Position	P_i (0)	P_i (2)
Professors	22.0	26.7
Associate Professors	17.5	22.3
Assistant Professors	12.2	18.3
Instructors	10.9	16.1
Totals	62.6	83.4
Index	100.0	$\frac{83.4}{62.6} \times 100 = 133.23$

(2) Fixed Weight Aggregate Price Index

Position	P_i (0) Q_i (1)	P_i (2) Q_i (1)
Professors	22.0 x 100 = 2,200.0	26.7 x 100 = 2,670.0
Associate Professors	17.5 x 309 = 5,407.5	22.3 x 309 = 6,890.7
Assistant Professors	12.2 x 341 = 4,160.2	18.3 x 341 = 6,240.3
Instructors	10.9 x 221 = 2,408.9	16.1 x 221 = 3,558.1
Totals	14,176.6	19,359.1
Index	100.0	$\frac{19,359.1}{14,176.6}$ x 100 = 136.56

(b) Percentage growth rate in nominal salaries for assistant professors over 8-year period 1972 to 1980):

$$\frac{\$18.3 - \$12.2}{\$12.2} \times 100 = 50.0\%$$

(c) Using the Consumer Price Index to deflate nominal income:

Real salaries (in constant 1980 thousands of dollars) $= \frac{\$18.3}{197.5} \times 100 = \$9,266$

Real salaries (in constant 1972 thousands of dollars) $= \frac{\$12.2}{118.1} \times 100 = \$10,330$

(d) Percentage growth in real salaries for assistant professors over 8-year period 1972 to 1980):

$$\frac{\$9,266 - \$10,330}{\$10,330} \times 100 = -10.3\%$$

(e) Over the 8-year period the salaries of assistant professors at this university have failed to keep pace with changes in prices, as measured by the Consumer Price Index. In this period, their purchasing power has diminished by 10.3%.

II. The following data represent the annual sales revenues (in millions of dollars) over the 13-year period 1975 to 1987 for Ethel's Originals, a manufacturer of junior-sized dresses:

Year	1975	1976	1977	1978	1979	1980	1981	1982	1983	1984	1985	1986	1987
Sales Revenues	0.7	0.6	1.1	0.9	1.2	1.5	1.4	1.3	1.6	1.8	1.4	1.5	1.7

(a) Plot the data on a chart.

(b) Fit a least-squares trend line to the data and plot the line on the chart.

(c) What is the least-squares trend forecast for 1988?

(d) Using a smoothing coefficient of .25, exponentially smooth the series and plot the results on the chart.

(e) What is the exponentially smoothed forecast for the trend in 1988?

(f) Fit a 7-year moving average to the data and plot the result on the chart.

(g) Determine the cyclical-irregular relatives and plot the results on a separate chart.

(h) Convert the annual least-squares trend equation to a monthly trend equation and shift the origin to July 15, 1980.

(i) What is the least-squares trend projection for November 1988?

(j) If the seasonal index for November is .950, what would be the forecast for sales revenue in November 1988?

(k) Use the MAD to compare the annual least-squares trend equation to the exponential smoothing model.

SOLUTION

(a)

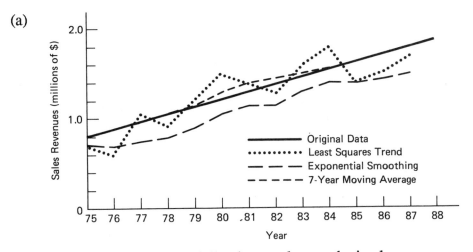

(b) Using the computer, the following results are obtained:

$$n = 13 \quad \Sigma X_i = 0 \quad \Sigma Y_i = 16.7 \quad \Sigma X_i^2 = 182.0 \quad \Sigma X_i Y_i = 15.0$$

since n is odd

$$b_1 = \frac{\Sigma X_i Y_i}{\Sigma X_i^2} = \frac{15.0}{182.0} = .082 \text{ and } b_0 = \overline{Y} \cong 1.285$$

so that $\hat{Y}_i = 1.285 + .082 X_i$

where origin = 1981 and X units = 1 year.

(c) The least-squares trend forecast for 1988 is:

1988: $\hat{Y}_{14} = 1.285 + .082 \ (7) \cong 1.86$ millions of dollars.

(d) To exponentially smooth a series we have

$$\varepsilon_i = W Y_i + (1 - W) \ \varepsilon_{i-1}$$

where the smoothed value of the ith period, ε_i, is a function of the observed value in the ith period (Y_i), the smoothed value from the previous period

(ε_{i-1}), and the smoothing coefficient (W). Using a computer, the following results are obtained:

Period = i	Year	Y_i	ε_i
1	1975	0.70	0.70
2	1976	0.60	0.67
3	1977	1.10	0.78
4	1978	0.90	0.81
5	1979	1.20	0.91
6	1980	1.50	1.06
7	1981	1.40	1.14
8	1982	1.30	1.18
9	1983	1.60	1.29
10	1984	1.80	1.41
11	1985	1.40	1.41
12	1986	1.50	1.43
13	1987	1.70	1.50

(e) The exponentially smoothed trend forecast for 1988 is equivalent to the smoothed value for the previous period, 1987. Thus,

$$\hat{Y}_{1988} = \varepsilon_{1987} = 1.50 \text{ millions of dollars.}$$

(f) Using a computer, the following 7-year moving average is obtained:

Period = i	Y_i	7-Year Moving Total	7-Year Moving Average
1	0.70	* . *	* . *
2	0.60	* . *	* . *
3	1.10	* . *	* . *
4	0.90	7.40	1.06
5	1.20	8.00	1.14
6	1.50	9.00	1.29
7	1.40	9.70	1.39
8	1.30	10.20	1.46
9	1.60	10.50	1.50
10	1.80	10.70	1.53
11	1.40	* . *	* . *
12	1.50	* . *	* . *
13	1.70	* . *	* . *

(g) Using a computer, the cyclical-irregular relatives are determined as follows:

X_i	Year	Y_i	$Y_i = b_0 + b_1 X_i$	$Y_i/\hat{Y}_i$
−6.0	1975	0.70	0.79	0.886
−5.0	1976	0.60	0.87	0.688
−4.0	1977	1.10	0.95	1.152
−3.0	1978	0.90	1.04	0.868
−2.0	1979	1.20	1.12	1.072
−1.0	1980	1.50	1.20	1.248
0.0	1981	1.40	1.28	1.090
1.0	1982	1.30	1.37	0.951
2.0	1983	1.60	1.45	1.104
3.0	1984	1.80	1.53	1.175
4.0	1985	1.40	1.61	0.867
5.0	1986	1.50	1.70	0.884
6.0	1987	1.70	1.78	0.956
7.0	1988	* . *	1.86	* . *
8.0	1989	* . *	1.94	* . *
9.0	1990	* . *	2.03	* . *

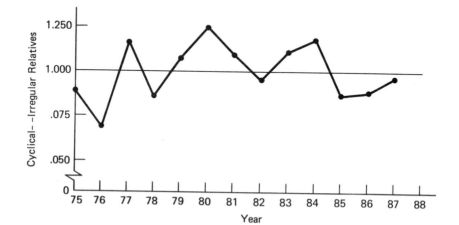

(h) To convert the annual least-squares trend equation to a monthly trend equation we divide the intercept by 12 and the slope by 144. Thus,

$$\hat{Y}_i = \frac{1.285}{12} + \frac{.082}{144}X_i = .1071 + .00057X_i$$

where origin = June 30–July 1, 1981 and X units = 1 month.

To shift to the middle of the month, July, we have

$$\hat{Y}_i = .1071 + .00057 \, (X_i + 0.5)$$

so that

$$\hat{Y}_i = .1074 + .00057X_i$$

where origin = July 15, 1981 and X units = 1 month.

(i) To obtain the least-squares trend projection for November 1988, let $X_i = 88$, since the month of interest occurs 88 months after the origin month (July 1981). Thus,

$$\hat{Y}_i = .1074 + (.00057) \, (88) = .1576 \text{ millions of dollars or } \$157,600.$$

(j) If the seasonal index for November is .950, the forecast of sales revenue in November 1988 is $\hat{Y}_i$ times the seasonal index = (.1576) (.950) = .1497 millions of dollars or $149,700.

(k) $$MAD = \frac{\sum_{i=1}^{n} | Y_i - \hat{Y}_i |}{n}$$

Linear Trend Model: $MAD = \frac{2.13}{13} = 0.164$

Exponential Smoothing Model: $MAD = \frac{2.57}{12} = 0.214$

(*Note:* First year is excluded.)

Historically, the linear trend model has fit the data better.

REVIEW PROBLEMS

I. The following table presents the prices paid by typical families of four for selected nonfrozen breakfast juices purchased at supermarkets in a large city:

Juice	Quantity* and Price**	Year		
		1974	1977	1980
Apple	Q	3.1	3.9	3.7
	P	.78	1.10	1.39
Orange	Q	4.5	4.2	4.8
	P	.53	.69	1.20
Pineapple	Q	2.4	2.8	2.7
	P	.61	.80	.92
Prune	Q	1.0	1.1	1.3
	P	.27	.39	.59

*Q = in thousands of units.
**P = in dollars per unit.

Moreover, the following table presents the Consumer Price Index for food and beverages compiled for the geographic region of interest:

	Year		
Consumer Price Index (1967 = 100.0)	1974	1977	1980
	121.7	163.3	202.5

(a) Using 1974 as the "base price" year, construct the following indexes of prices paid by typical families of four for selected nonfrozen breakfast juices for the year 1980:

    (1) Simple Aggregate

    (2) "Fixed" Weights (using 1977 as the weight period).

(b) Determine the percentage growth rate in "nominal" prices paid for apple juice over the 6-year period 1974 to 1980.

(c) Deflate the 1974 and 1980 figures by the Consumer Price Index for those years.

(d) Determine the percentage growth rate in "real" prices paid for apple juice over the 6-year period 1974 to 1980.

SOLUTION

(a) Let the base year period 1974 be given the code 0. The index in the base year period is 100.0.
Let 1977 be given the code 1.
Let 1980 be given the code 2.

(1) Simple Aggregate Price Index:

$$I_{SA}^{(2)} = \frac{\Sigma P_i^{(2)}}{\Sigma P_i^{(0)}} \times 100 = 187.21$$

(2) Fixed Weight Aggregate Price Index:

$$I_{FWA}^{(2)} = \frac{\Sigma P_i^{(2)}Q_i^{(1)}}{\Sigma P_i^{(0)}Q_i^{(1)}} \times 100 = 188.18$$

(b) Percentage growth rate in nominal prices paid for apple juice:

$$\frac{\$1.39 - \$.78}{\$.78} \times 100 = 78.2\%$$

(c) Deflating nominal prices:

$$\frac{\text{Real Prices}}{\text{(in constant 1980 \$)}} = \frac{\$1.39}{202.5} \times 100 = \$.69$$

$$\frac{\text{Real Prices}}{\text{(in constant 1974 \$)}} = \frac{\$.78}{121.7} \times 100 = \$.64$$

(d) Percentage growth rate in real prices paid for apple juice:

$$\frac{\$.69 - \$.64}{\$.64} \times 100 = 7.8\%$$

II. The following data represent the sales revenues (in millions of dollars) over the 10-year period 1978 through 1987 for the Little Angela Corporation—the manufacturer of the famous Lovable Lori, Kuddly Kathy and Sweet Sharyn dolls and accessories:

Year	1978	1979	1980	1981	1982	1983	1984	1985	1986	1987
Sales Revenues	8.7	8.3	9.6	10.0	12.5	12.7	14.1	15.0	16.5	17.7

(a) Plot the data on a chart.

(b) Fit a least-squares trend line to the data and plot the line on the chart.

(c) What is the least-squares trend forecast for 1988?

(d) Using a smoothing coefficient, of .40, exponentially smooth the series and plot the results on the chart.

(e) What is the exponentially smoothed forecast for the trend in 1988?

(f) Use the Holt-Winters forecasting method with $U = 0.3$ and $V = 0.3$. What is your forecast for the year 1988?

(g) Fit a second-order autoregressive model to the data and test for the significance of the second-order autoregressive parameter. If the model is appropriate, what is your forecast for the year 1988?

(h) Convert the annual least-squares trend equation to a monthly trend equation and shift the origin to July 15, 1978.

(i) What is the least-squares trend projection for July 1988 and for December 1988?

(j) If the seasonal index for July is .750 and if the seasonal index for December is 1.225, what would be the forecasts for sales revenue in July 1988 and in December 1988?

(k) Use the MAD to compare the annual least-squares trend equation to the exponential smoothing model.

SOLUTION

(a)

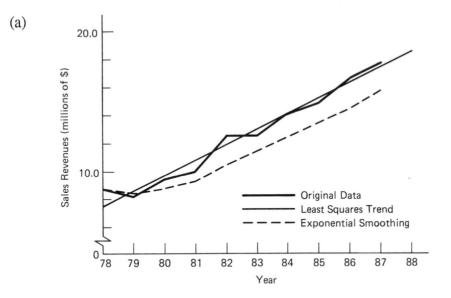

(b) n = 10. Since n is even, we have

$$b_1 = \frac{\Sigma X_i Y_i - \dfrac{(\Sigma X_i)(\Sigma Y_i)}{n}}{\Sigma X_i^2 - \dfrac{(\Sigma X_i)^2}{n}} = 1.0782$$

and

$$b_0 = \overline{Y} - b_1\overline{X} = 7.6582$$

so that

$$\hat{Y}_i = 7.6582 + 1.0782X_i$$

where origin = 1978 and X units = 1 year

(c) Least-squares trend forecast for 1988 is:

$$1988: \hat{Y}_{11} = 7.6582 + (1.0782)(10) \cong 18.44 \text{ millions of dollars}$$

(d) Using an exponential smoothing coefficient W = 0.40, we have:

Period = i	Year	Y_i	ε_i
1	1978	8.70	8.70
2	1979	8.30	8.54
3	1980	9.60	8.96
4	1981	10.00	9.38
5	1982	12.50	10.63
6	1983	12.70	11.46
7	1984	14.10	12.51
8	1985	15.00	13.51
9	1986	16.50	14.70
10	1987	17.70	15.90

(e) $\hat{Y}_{1988} = \varepsilon_{1987} = 15.90$ millions of dollars

(f) Using the Holt-Winters method:

Year	i	Y_i	$U(\varepsilon_{i-1}+T_{i-1})+(1-U)Y_i=\varepsilon_i$		$VT_{i-1}+(1-V)(\varepsilon_i-\varepsilon_{i-1})=T_i$	
1978	1	8.70		....		....
1979	2	8.30		8.30		−0.40
1980	3	9.60	0.3(8.30+(−0.4))+0.7(9.6)	= 9.09	0.3(−0.4)+0.7(9.09−8.30)	= 0.43
1981	4	10.00	0.3(9.09+.43)+0.7(10.00)	= 9.86	0.3(.43)+0.7(9.86−9.09)	= 0.67
1982	5	12.50	0.3(9.86+.67)+0.7(12.50)	=11.91	0.3(.67)+0.7(11.91−9.86)	= 1.64
1983	6	12.70	0.3(11.91+1.64)+0.7(12.70)	=12.96	0.3(1.64)+0.7(12.96−11.91)	= 1.23
1984	7	14.10	0.3(12.96+1.23)+0.7(14.10)	=14.13	0.3(1.23)+0.7(14.13−12.96)	= 1.19
1985	8	15.00	0.3(14.13+1.19)+0.7(15.00)	=15.10	0.3(1.19)+0.7(15.10−14.13)	= 1.04
1986	9	16.50	0.3(15.10+1.04)+0.7(16.50)	=16.39	0.3(1.04)+0.7(16.39−15.10)	= 1.22
1987	10	17.70	0.3(16.39+1.22)+0.7(17.70)	=17.67	0.3(1.22)+0.7(17.67−16.39)	= 1.26

Set $\varepsilon_2 = Y_2 = 8.30$

and $T_2 = Y_2 - Y_1 = 8.30 - 8.70 = -0.4$

Our smoothing constants are $U = 0.3$ and $V = 0.3$. These values are used to obtain the remaining ε_i and T_i values as shown in the above table.

To forecast $j = 1$ year into the future we have

$$\hat{Y}_{n+j} = \varepsilon_n + j\,(T_n)$$

1988: 1 year ahead $\quad \hat{Y}_{11} = \varepsilon_{10} + 1\,(T_{10})$

$$\hat{Y}_{11} = 17.67 + 1\,(1.26)$$

$$\hat{Y}_{11} = 18.93 \text{ millions of dollars}$$

(g) Using Minitab we have:

```
-- READ C1
COLUMN          C1
COUNT          10
       8.7000        8.3000        9.6000       10.0000    .    .    .

-- NOTE 2ND ORDER MODEL

-- LAG 1 IN C1,PUT IN C2

-- LAG 2 IN C1,PUT IN C3

-- PRINT C1-C3
```

COLUMN	C1	C2	C3
COUNT	10	10	10
ROW			
1	8.7000************************		
2	8.3000	8.7000************	
3	9.6000	8.3000	8.7000
4	10.0000	9.6000	8.3000
5	12.5000	10.0000	9.6000
6	12.7000	12.5000	10.0000
7	14.1000	12.7000	12.5000
8	15.0000	14.1000	12.7000
9	16.5000	15.0000	14.1000
10	17.7000	16.5000	15.0000

```
-- REGRESS C1 WITH 2 PREDICTORS C2 C3

    8 CASES USED
    2 CASES CONTAINED MISSING VALUES
```

The fitted second-order autoregressive model is

$$\hat{Y}_i = 0.823 + 0.438 Y_{i-1} + 0.641 Y_{i-2}$$

To test for the significance of the second-order autoregressive parameter:

$H_0: \psi_2 = 0$

$H_1: \psi_2 \neq 0$

$\alpha = .05$ (2-tail)

$$Z \cong \frac{\hat{\psi}_2}{S_{\hat{\psi}_2}} = \frac{0.641}{0.281} = 2.28$$

Since $Z = 2.28 > 1.96$, we may reject H_0 and conclude that the second-order term significantly contributes to the overall model. Since the model is appropriate we may use it to forecast sales revenues for the year 1988:

$$\hat{Y}_{n+j} = 0.823 + 0.438 \, \hat{Y}_{n+j-1} + 0.641 \, \hat{Y}_{n+j-2}$$

1988: 1 year ahead:

$$\hat{Y}_{11} = 0.823 + 0.438\ (17.7) + 0.641\ (16.5) = 19.15 \text{ millions of dollars}$$

(h) To convert the annual least-squares equation to a monthly trend equation and then shift the origin to July 15, 1978, we have:

$$\hat{Y}_i = \frac{7.6582}{12} + \frac{1.0782}{144} X_i = .6382 + .00749 X_i$$

so that

$$\hat{Y}_i = .6382 + .00749\ (X_i + 0.5)$$

and thus

$$\hat{Y}_i = .6419 + .00749 X_i$$

where origin = July 15, 1978 and X units = 1 month

(i) The least-squares trend projections for July 1988 and December 1988 are:

July 1988: $\hat{Y}_i = .6419 + (.00749)\ (120) = 1.541$ millions of dollars
December 1988: $\hat{Y}_i = .6419 + (.00749)\ (125) = 1.578$ millions of dollars

(j) To forecast sales revenues for July 1988 and December 1988 we have:

July 1988: $(1.541)\ (.750) = 1.156$ millions of dollars
December 1988: $(1.578)\ (1.225) = 1.944$ millions of dollars

(k) For the linear trend model, MAD $= \dfrac{4.26}{10} = 0.426$

For the exponential smoothing model, MAD $= \dfrac{11.29}{9} = 1.254$
(*Note:* first year is excluded)

Historically, the linear trend model has fit the data better.

19

Statistical Applications in Quality and Productivity Management

We end our discussion of statistical concepts and methods by presenting some statistical applications in quality and productivity management. Introduced with a discussion of W. Edwards Deming's approach to management, we will illustrate several types of control charts which researchers use to study variation in a product or service. We will show how a control chart can be used to reveal past performances, to evaluate present conditions, and to make decisions about the need for taking corrective action.

MULTIPLE CHOICE

1. What type of managerial style emphasizes the continuous improvement of the quality of a product?

    a. Management by doing
    b. Management by directing
    c. Management by control
    d. Management by process

2. The control chart is a means of studying variation in a product or service by focusing on

   a. the order in which items are collected.
   b. the box and whisker plot
   c. the degree to which workers are given control over the product or service.
   d. differences in the quality of products produced by different workers.

3. The principal focus of the control chart is the attempt to separate "special or assignable causes" of variation from "common causes" of variation. What cause of variation can be reduced only by changing a system?

   a. assignable causes of variation
   b. common causes of variation
   c. a and b are both possible answers
   d. neither a nor b are possible answers.

4. Once the control limits are set for a control chart a researcher attempts to

   a. discern patterns that might exist in values over time.
   b. determine whether any points fall outside the control limits.
   c. exert greater control over the production process.
   d. a and b.

5. Which of the following types of control charts would suggest that a researcher needs to study a process that appears to be operating improperly?

   a. a control chart with a series of consecutive points that are above the average value as well as a series of consecutive points that are below the average value.
   b. a control chart in which no points fall outside the 3 standard deviation limits of variability.
   c. a control chart with several points falling outside the 3 standard deviation control limits
   d. a and c.

6. Which of the following is not a part of Deming's theory of management by process?

    a. Break down barriers between staff areas.
    b. Institute training on the job.
    c. Eliminate a merit system.
    d. Institute slogans, exhortations, and targets for the work force.

7. In acceptance sampling the rejection of a lot that should have been accepted is called

    a. a Type I error.
    b. a Type II error.
    c. the producer's risk.
    d. a and c.

8. The most common control chart will set "control limits" that are within $\pm$ _____ standard deviations of the statistical measure of interest.

    a. 0.5.
    b. 1.0.
    c. 2.0.
    d. 3.0.

9. A sampling procedure in which a decision is made to accept an entire lot of a product or service based only on a sample of the lot is called

    a. mass inspection.
    b. acceptance sampling.
    c. all or none inspection.
    d. rejection sampling.

EXAMPLES

I. A soft-drink machine dispenses liquid that historically has a mean of 16 ounces with a standard deviation of .80 ounces. A sample of 20 consecutively filled cups is selected. The ounces contained in each cup are recorded below in row sequence (from left to right).

17.62	17.45	17.30	17.35	17.25
16.65	16.35	16.40	16.20	16.10
15.85	15.70	15.75	15.50	15.30
15.25	15.15	15.20	14.85	14.42

(a) Set up a control chart for these data using 3 standard deviation limits.
(b) What conclusions can you reach about whether the process is in control?
(c) Suppose that you do not wish to assume that the process mean and process standard deviation have remained at their historical values. Set up a control chart for this situation.
(d) Compare the control charts obtained in parts (a) and (c). What conclusions can you reach?

SOLUTION

(a) Run Chart for Ounces of Soft Drink Dispensed.

Since the process mean and standard deviation are known, the center line would be located at the process mean. The upper control limit (UCL) would be the process mean + 3 standard deviations while the lower control limit (LCL) would be the process mean − 3 standard deviations.

process mean $\pm$ 3 standard deviations
$= 16 \pm 3 \, (.8)$
$= 16 \pm 2.4$

Thus, UCL = 18.4 and LCL = 13.6.

(b) This control chart shows that none of the 20 points fall outside of the control limits. However, there is a clear downward pattern indicating that the amount of soft-drink being dispensed is decreasing. This chart indicates that corrective action should be taken to determine the special cause in this problem.

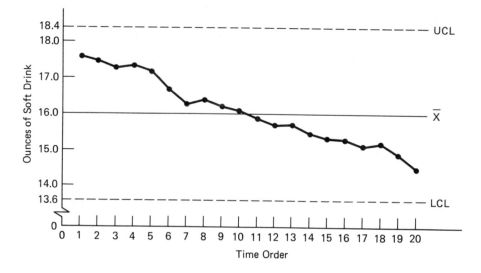

Run Chart for Ounces of Soft Drink Dispensed

(c) The Run Chart when the Process Average and Process Standard Deviation
Are Unknown.

Since we do not wish to assume that the process mean nor the process
standard deviation have remained at the given values, we will use the sample
mean, $\overline{X}$, as an estimate of the process mean, and we will estimate the
standard deviation by using the moving range.

Observation	Sample	High	Low	Moving Range
17.62	1	17.62	17.45	0.17
17.45	2	17.45	17.30	0.15
17.30	3	17.35	17.30	0.05
17.35	4	17.35	17.25	0.10
17.25	5	17.25	16.65	0.60
16.65	6	16.65	16.35	0.30
16.35	7	16.40	16.35	0.05
16.40	8	16.40	16.20	0.20
16.20	9	16.20	16.10	0.10
16.10	10	16.10	15.85	0.25
15.85	11	15.85	15.70	0.15
15.70	12	15.75	15.70	0.05
15.75	13	15.75	15.50	0.25
15.50	14	15.50	15.30	0.20
15.30	15	15.30	15.25	0.05
15.25	16	15.25	15.15	0.10
15.15	17	15.20	15.15	0.05
15.20	18	15.20	14.85	0.35
14.85	19	14.85	14.42	0.43
14.42	20			

$$\sum_{i=1}^{K} X_i = 321.64 \qquad\qquad \sum_{i=1}^{K-1} MR_i = 3.6$$

Thus, $\bar{X} = \dfrac{321.64}{20} = 16.082$ and $\overline{MR} = \dfrac{3.6}{19} = 0.189$

We may set up the control limits as

$$\bar{X} \pm \frac{3\,\overline{MR}}{d_2}$$

$$= 16.082 \pm \frac{3\,(.189)}{1.128}$$

$$= 16.082 \pm \frac{.567}{1.128}$$

$$= 16.082 \pm .5027$$

Thus, LCL = 15.579 and UCL = 16.585

(d) The revised control chart based on the new control limits and center line differs noticeably from the first control chart set up in (a). The moving range used to construct the revised control chart emphasizes variation between consecutive values. Consequently, when there is a trend in the data, as we concluded in (a), it is better to use control limits based on the moving range instead of ones based on the sample standard deviation so we can highlight the out of control situation.

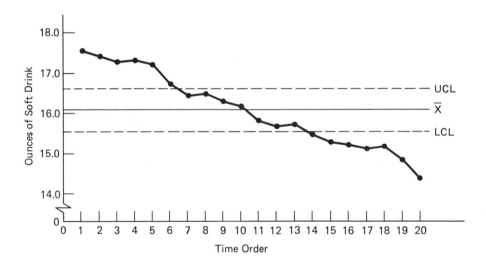

Run Chart for Ounces of Soft Drink
When Process Mean and Standard Deviation Are Unknown

II. The foreman in a car factory wanted to study the amount of time it took workers to perform a final inspection of new cars (i.e., brakes, lights, windshield wipers, etc.). He recorded data over a three week period using samples of five inspections from a certain shift each day. The results of his study are recorded on the following page:

Day	Sample Average (in minutes) $\overline{X}_i$	Sample Range (in minutes) R_i
1	6.73	3.75
2	6.50	3.50
3	6.26	3.00
4	7.26	3.25
5	7.41	3.35
6	7.65	3.50
7	7.00	3.15
8	6.85	3.42
9	6.55	3.27
10	6.72	3.10
11	7.37	3.24
12	7.42	3.32
13	7.51	3.48
14	6.79	3.18
15	6.75	3.38
16	6.62	3.24
17	6.72	3.09
18	7.32	3.32
19	7.52	3.47
20	7.58	3.45
21	6.85	3.25

$$\sum_{i=1}^{K} \overline{X}_i = 147.38 \qquad \sum_{i=1}^{K} R_i = 69.71$$

(a) Set up a $\overline{X}$ control chart for the average inspection time and determine whether the inspection time is in control.

(b) What can you conclude on the basis of this $\overline{X}$ control chart?

(c) Set up an R chart and determine whether the process is in control in reference to the range.

SOLUTION

(a) Control Chart for the mean ($\overline{X}$).

Since we do not know the process mean or process standard deviation, we will use the sample data to estimate each, and we will set up the control limits by the following equation:

$$\overline{\overline{X}} \pm \frac{3\ \overline{R}}{d_2\sqrt{n}}$$

where

$$\overline{\overline{X}} = \frac{\sum\limits_{i=1}^{K}\overline{X}_i}{K} \qquad \text{and} \qquad \overline{R} = \frac{\sum\limits_{i=1}^{K}R_i}{K}$$

where $\overline{X}_i$ = the sample mean of n observations at time i
and R_i = the range of n observations at time i

so that

$$LCL = \overline{\overline{X}} - \frac{3\ \overline{R}}{d_2\sqrt{n}}$$

and

$$UCL = \overline{\overline{X}} + \frac{3\ \overline{R}}{d_2\sqrt{n}}$$

For the data given,

$$\sum\limits_{i=1}^{K}\overline{X}_i = 147.38 \qquad \text{and} \qquad \sum\limits_{i=1}^{K}R_i = 69.71$$

Thus,

$$\bar{\bar{X}} = \frac{147.38}{21} = 7.018 \qquad \text{and} \qquad \bar{R} = \frac{69.71}{21} = 3.32$$

Using the equation

$$\bar{\bar{X}} \pm \frac{3\,\bar{R}}{d_2\sqrt{n}}$$

we have

$$7.018 \pm \frac{3\,(3.32)}{2.326\,\sqrt{5}}$$

$$7.018 \pm \frac{9.60}{2.326\,(2.236)}$$

$$7.018 \pm \frac{9.60}{5.20}$$

$$7.018 \pm 1.846$$

Thus, LCL = 5.172 and UCL = 8.864

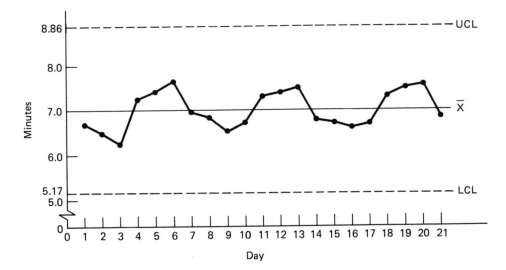

$\bar{X}$ Chart for Average Inspection Time

(b) Although this $\overline{X}$ control chart does not show any points outside the control limits, there is a pattern requiring closer examination. As this shows, there are three series of consecutive points with an increasing trend above the mean as well as three series of consecutive points with a decreasing trend below the mean. Since days 4-6, 11-13, and 18-20 correspond to Thursday-Saturday, these data suggest that inspection times increase as the work week progresses toward the weekend. The best performance times are between Mondays and Wednesdays.

(c) The R Chart for Inspection Times.

We may set up control limits for the range over K consecutive sequences or periods of time using the following equation:

$$\overline{R} \pm \frac{3d_3 \, \overline{R}}{d_2}$$

$$\text{where } \overline{R} = \frac{\sum_{i=1}^{K} R_i}{K}$$

so that

$$\text{LCL} = \overline{R} - \frac{3d_3 \, \overline{R}}{d_2} = 3.32 - \frac{3\,(.864)\,(3.32)}{2.326}$$

$$= 3.32 - 3.6997$$

Since the resulting value is less than zero, the LCL does not exist.

$$\text{UCL} = \overline{R} + \frac{3d_3 \, \overline{R}}{d_2} = 3.32 + \frac{3\,(.864)\,(3.32)}{2.326}$$

$$= 3.32 + 3.6997$$

$$= 7.02$$

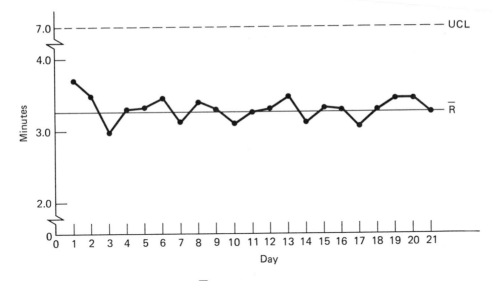

The R̄ Chart for Inspection Times

The control chart does not show any individual ranges outside the control limits. However, there does appear to be a slight cyclical pattern suggesting that the ranges are slightly higher for weekends (i.e., days 5, 6, 12, 13, 19, 20).

III. In addition to studying the time it took workers to perform a final inspection of new cars, the foreman of the car factory also wanted to study the proportion of brake lights that were not working properly. A random sample of 50 cars was selected each day. The proportion of brake lights that were not working properly for each day in the three week period are shown on the following page:

Day	Proportion
1	.02
2	.06
3	.04
4	.02
5	.04
6	.04
7	.02
8	.02
9	.02
10	.04
11	.04
12	.04
13	.02
14	.04
15	.04
16	.02
17	.02
18	.02
19	.02
20	.04
21	.02

(a) Set up a p chart for the proportion of brake lights that were not working properly.

(b) Based on this chart, would you conclude that the process is in statistical control?

SOLUTION

(a) The p Chart.

The proportion of non-working brake lights is not known, so we estimate the sample proportion using the following equation:

$$\bar{p} \pm 3 \sqrt{\frac{\bar{p}\,(1 - \bar{p})}{n}}$$

where

$$\bar{p} = \frac{\sum_{i=1}^{K} P_{s_i}}{K}$$

where

p_{s_i} = proportion for sample i

K = number of samples taken

For these data, K = 21 and $\sum_{i=1}^{K} P_{s_i} = 0.64$

Thus, $\bar{p} = \frac{.64}{21} = .0305$

We may set up the control limits using the equation:

$$\bar{p} \pm 3 \sqrt{\frac{\bar{p}\,(1 - \bar{p})}{n}}$$

$$= .0305 \pm 3 \sqrt{\frac{(.0305)\,(.9695)}{50}}$$

$$= .0305 \pm 3\,(.0243)$$

$$= .0305 \pm .0729$$

Thus, UCL = 0.1034, and the LCL does not exist.

(b) This p chart seems to show a process in a state of statistical control, with the individual points distributed around $\bar{p}$ without any pattern. This also shows that all the points are well within the control limits.

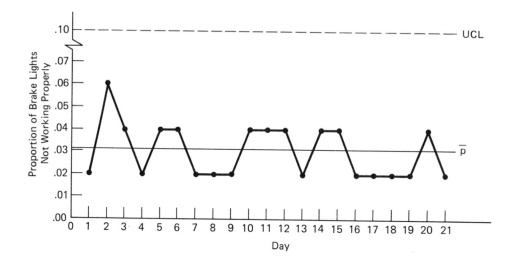

P Chart for the Proportion of Brake Lights Not Working Properly

IV. The manager of a printing service would like to study the number of blank sheets produced per ream of paper used in the copying process. A record of the number of blank sheets produced in 50 reams of paper are shown on the following page:

Ream	Number of Blanks	Ream	Number of Blanks
1	3	26	6
2	4	27	7
3	3	28	6
4	5	29	7
5	4	30	5
6	3	31	6
7	4	32	7
8	5	33	6
9	4	34	6
10	4	35	7
11	5	36	7
12	6	37	6
13	4	38	6
14	4	39	7
15	4	40	7
16	5	41	7
17	6	42	6
18	5	43	8
19	6	44	8
20	5	45	7
21	5	46	8
22	6	47	9
23	7	48	8
24	6	49	9
25	5	50	9

(a) Set up a c chart for the number of blank sheets produced per ream.
(b) What conclusions can you draw about the printing process on the basis of this c chart?

SOLUTION

(a) The c chart.

Since we do not have a prior estimate for the number of occurrences per unit (c_0), we estimate the number of occurrences (c) from the data as

$$\bar{c} = \frac{\sum_{i=1}^{K} c_i}{K}$$

where

K is the number of units sampled
c_i is the number of occurrences in unit i

For these data, K = 50 and $\sum_{i=1}^{K} c_i = 293$

Thus, $\bar{c} = \frac{293}{50} = 5.86$

The control limits for the average number of occurrences would then be obtained from

$$\bar{c} \pm 3 \sqrt{\bar{c}}$$

so that we have

$$5.86 \pm 3 \sqrt{5.86}$$

$$= \quad 5.86 \pm (3)(2.42)$$

$$= \quad 5.86 \pm 7.26$$

Thus, UCL = 13.12 and the LCL does not exist.

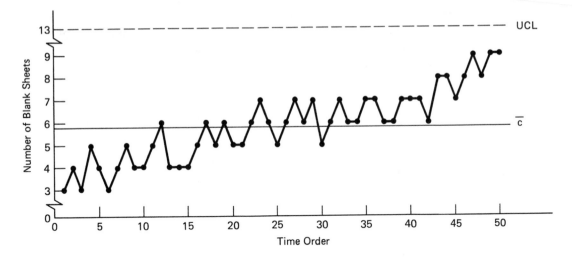

C̄ Chart for Number of Blank Sheets Produced Per Ream

(b) Although the c chart does not show any points outside the control limits, there is a clear pattern to the number of blank sheets produced per ream over time. Batches of copies produced in the first half of the sequence contain less than the average number of blank sheets per ream, while batches of copies produced in the second half of the sequence contain more than the average number of blank sheets. Thus, the manager of the printing service should try to determine the special causes that have produced this pattern of variation.

REVIEW PROBLEMS

I. The field director of a public opinion poll wanted to study the number of coding errors that data entry clerks made with the data for a pilot study of 50 respondents. The number of errors made per 320 columns of data for each case is shown in the table on the following page.

Case	Number of Errors	Case	Number of Errors
1	3	26	4
2	3	27	4
3	2	28	3
4	2	29	4
5	1	30	4
6	2	31	5
7	1	32	4
8	1	33	4
9	2	34	4
10	2	35	5
11	3	36	4
12	3	37	5
13	2	38	4
14	3	39	5
15	2	40	5
16	3	41	4
17	3	42	5
18	2	43	6
19	2	44	5
20	3	45	5
21	2	46	6
22	3	47	5
23	4	48	5
24	3	49	6
25	3	50	6

(a) Set up a c chart for the number of errors made per case.
(b) Do you think that the process is in a state of statistical control? Should the field director investigate the data entry procedure?

SOLUTION

(a) We assume that the size of each sample unit remains constant (320 columns of data) and set up control limits for the number of occurrences using the normal approximation to the Poisson distribution. Since no prior estimate is available for the number of occurrences per unit (c_0), the average number of occurrences (c) would be estimated from the data as

$$\bar{c} = \frac{\sum\limits_{i=1}^{K} c_i}{K}$$

where

K is the number of units sampled

c_i is the number of occurrences in unit i

Thus, the control limits for the average number of occurrences would be

$$\bar{c} \pm 3 \sqrt{\bar{c}}$$

For these data, K = 50 and $\sum\limits_{i=1}^{K} c_i = 177$

Thus,

$$\bar{c} = \frac{177}{50} = 3.54$$

so that we have

$$3.54 \pm 3 \sqrt{3.54}$$

$$= \quad 3.54 \pm 3 \,(1.88)$$

$$= \quad 3.54 \pm 5.64$$

Thus, UCL = 9.18, and LCL does not exist.

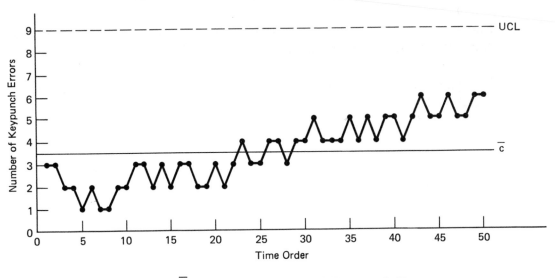

$\bar{C}$ Chart for Number of Keypunch Errors

(b) Although this c chart does not show any points outside the control limits, there is a clear pattern over time. The cases entered in the beginning of this sequence have fewer than the average number of errors, while cases entered in the latter half of the sequence have more than the average number of errors. Thus, the field director should investigate the data entry process to determine the special cause that has produced this pattern of variation.

II. A machine used to dispense cookie dough produces cookies that have a diameter that historically have a process average of 2.5 inches with a process standard deviation of .25 inches. A sample of 30 consecutive cookies manufactured by this process is selected. The diameters of the cookies are recorded below in row sequence (from left to right).

2.00	2.00	2.10	2.10	2.15
2.15	2.20	2.20	2.25	2.25
2.25	2.30	2.40	2.45	2.50
2.55	2.65	2.70	2.75	2.75
2.80	2.85	2.90	2.95	3.00
3.00	3.10	3.15	3.15	3.20

(a) Set up a control chart for these data using 3 standard deviation limits.
(b) What conclusions can you reach about whether the process is in control?

(c) Suppose that you do not wish to assume that the process mean and process standard deviation have remained at their historical values. Set up a control chart for this situation.

(d) Compare the control charts obtained in (a) and (c). What conclusions can you draw?

(a)

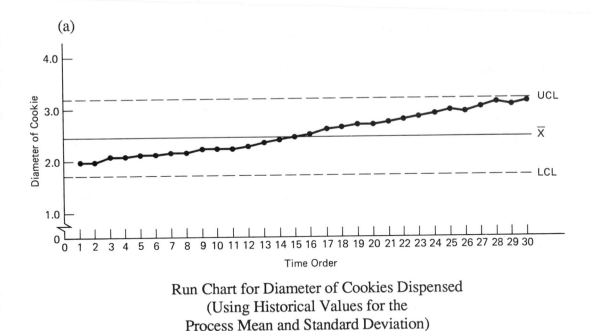

Run Chart for Diameter of Cookies Dispensed
(Using Historical Values for the
Process Mean and Standard Deviation)

(b) Although none of the 30 points fall outside the control limits, there is a clear upward pattern in the diameters of the cookies. This chart indicates that corrective action should be taken to determine the special cause in this problem.

(c) This is an example of the run chart when the process average and standard deviation are unknown. The sample mean, $\overline{X}$, will be used to estimate the process mean and the moving range, $\overline{MR}$, will be used to estimate the process standard deviation. Subsets of $n = 2$ will be used.

COMPUTATION OF THE MOVING RANGE

Observation	Sample	High	Low	Moving Range
2.00	1	2.00	2.00	0.00
2.00	2	2.00	2.10	0.10
2.10	3	2.10	2.10	0.00
2.10	4	2.10	2.15	0.05
2.15	5	2.15	2.15	0.00
2.15	6	2.15	2.20	0.05
2.20	7	2.20	2.20	0.00
2.20	8	2.20	2.25	0.05
2.25	9	2.25	2.25	0.00
2.25	10	2.25	2.25	0.00
2.25	11	2.25	2.30	0.05
2.30	12	2.30	2.40	0.10
2.40	13	2.40	2.45	0.05
2.45	14	2.45	2.50	0.05
2.50	15	2.50	2.55	0.05
2.55	16	2.55	2.65	0.10
2.65	17	2.65	2.70	0.05
2.70	18	2.70	2.75	0.05
2.75	19	2.75	2.75	0.00
2.75	20	2.75	2.80	0.05
2.80	21	2.80	2.85	0.05
2.85	22	2.85	2.90	0.05
2.90	23	2.90	2.95	0.05
2.95	24	2.95	3.00	0.05
3.00	25	3.00	3.00	0.00
3.00	26	3.00	3.10	0.10
3.10	27	3.10	3.15	0.05
3.15	28	3.15	3.15	0.00
3.15	29	3.15	3.20	0.05
3.20	30			

$$\sum_{i=1}^{K} X_i = 76.8$$

$$\sum_{i=1}^{K-1} MR_i = 1.20$$

Thus,

$$\bar{X} = \frac{76.8}{30} = 2.56$$

and

$$\overline{MR} = \frac{1.20}{29} = .041$$

Using $\bar{X} \pm \frac{3\,\overline{MR}}{d_2}$, we can set up control limits as

$$2.56 \pm \frac{3\,(.041)}{1.128}$$

$$= \quad 2.56 \pm \frac{.123}{1.128}$$

$$= \quad 2.56 \pm .109$$

Thus, the LCL = 2.45 and UCL = 2.65.

(d) The revised control chart, which uses the moving range, differs drastically from the run chart drawn for (a). As shown here, the moving range emphasizes the variation between consecutive values. In this case the out of control condition is highlighted by using the moving range.

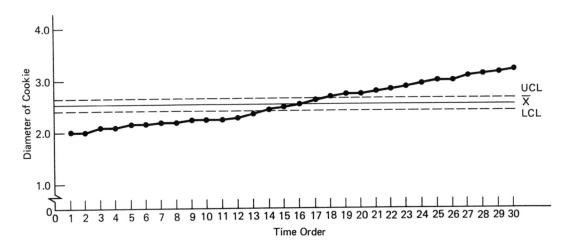

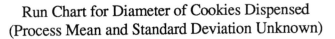

Run Chart for Diameter of Cookies Dispensed
(Process Mean and Standard Deviation Unknown)

Appendix: Review of Arithmetic and Algebra

In writing this text, we realize that there are wide differences in the mathematical background of students taking a basic business statistics course. Some students may have taken various courses in calculus and matrix algebra, while many other students may not have taken any mathematics courses since high school. The emphasis in this text is on the concepts of statistical methods as they can be applied in business. No mathematical prerequisite beyond algebra is needed, since no formal mathematical proofs are derived. However, a proper foundation in basic arithmetic and algebraic skills will enable the student to focus upon understanding the concepts of statistics rather than the mechanics of computing results.

With this goal in mind, we should make clear that the object of this appendix is merely to *review* arithmetic and algebra for those students whose basic skills have become "rusty" over a period of time. If students need to actually *learn* arithmetic and algebra, then this brief review will probably not provide enough depth.

In order to assess one's arithmetic and algebraic skills, we would suggest that each student take the following quiz at the *beginning* of the semester:

PART I   Fill in the correct answer.

1. $\dfrac{1}{\dfrac{2}{3}} =$

2. $.4^2 =$

3. $1 + \dfrac{2}{3} =$

4. $\left(\dfrac{1}{3}\right)^4 =$

5. $\dfrac{1}{5} =$ (in decimals)

6. $1 - (-.3) =$

7. $4 \times .2 \times (-8) =$

8. $\left(\dfrac{1}{4}\right) \times \left(\dfrac{2}{3}\right) =$

9. $\dfrac{1}{100} + \dfrac{1}{200} =$

10. $\sqrt{16} =$

PART II   Select the correct answer.

1. If $a = bc$, then $c =$

   (a) ab

   (b) $\dfrac{b}{a}$

   (c) $\dfrac{a}{b}$

   (d) None of the above.

2. If $x + y = z$, then $y =$

   (a) $\dfrac{z}{x}$

   (b) $z + x$

   (c) $z - x$

   (d) None of the above.

3. $x^3 \cdot x^2 =$

   (a) x^5
   (b) x^6
   (c) x^1
   (d) None of the above.

4. $x^0 =$

   (a) x
   (b) 1
   (c) 0
   (d) None of the above.

5. $x(y - z) =$

    (a) $xy - xz$

    (b) $xy - z$

    (c) $\dfrac{(y - z)}{x}$

    (d) None of the above.

6. $\dfrac{x + y}{z} =$

    (a) $\left(\dfrac{x}{z}\right) + y$

    (b) $\left(\dfrac{x}{z}\right) + \left(\dfrac{y}{z}\right)$

    (c) $x + \left(\dfrac{y}{z}\right)$

    (d) None of the above.

7. $\dfrac{x}{y + z} =$

    (a) $\left(\dfrac{x}{y}\right) + \left(\dfrac{1}{z}\right)$

    (b) $\left(\dfrac{x}{y}\right) + \left(\dfrac{x}{z}\right)$

    (c) $\dfrac{(y + z)}{x}$

    (d) None of the above.

8. If $x = 10$, $y = 5$, $z = 2$, $w = 20$,

    then $\dfrac{xy - z^2}{w} =$

    (a) 5

    (b) 2.3

    (c) 46

    (d) None of the above.

9. $\dfrac{8x^4}{4x^2} =$

    (a) $2x^2$

    (b) 2

    (c) $2x$

    (d) None of the above.

10. $\sqrt{\dfrac{x}{y}} =$

    (a) $\dfrac{\sqrt{y}}{\sqrt{x}}$

    (b) $\dfrac{\sqrt{1}}{\sqrt{xy}}$

    (c) $\dfrac{\sqrt{x}}{\sqrt{y}}$

    (d) None of the above.

The answers to both parts of this quiz appear at the end of this appendix.

REVIEW OF ARITHMETIC AND ALGEBRAIC OPERATIONS

A. *Symbols*

Each of the four basic arithmetic operations—addition, subtraction, multiplication, and division—are indicated by an appropriate symbol:

+	add	x	multiply
−	subtract	÷	divide

In addition to these operations, the following symbols are used to indicate equality or inequality:

=	equals	≠	not equal
≅	approximately equal to		
>	greater than	<	less than
≥ or $\geqq$	greater than or equal to		
≤ or $\leqq$	less than or equal to		

B. *Addition*

The process of addition refers to the summation or accumulation of a set of numbers. In adding numbers together, there are two basic principles or laws: the *commutative* law and the *associative* law.

The commutative law states that the order in which numbers are added is irrelevant. This can be seen in the following two examples:

$$1 + 2 = 3 \qquad x + y = z$$
$$2 + 1 = 3 \qquad y + x = z$$

In each example, it did not matter which number was added first and which was added second; the result was the same.

The associative law of addition states that in adding several numbers, any subgrouping of the numbers can be added first, last, or in the middle. This can be seen in the following example:

(1) $2 + 3 + 6 + 7 + 4 + 1 = 23$
(2) $(5) + (6 + 7) + 4 + 1 = 23$

(3) $5 + 13 + 5 = 23$

(4) $5 + 6 + 7 + 4 + 1 = 23$

In each of these cases the order in which the numbers have been added has no effect on the result.

C. *Subtraction*

The process of subtraction is the opposite or inverse of addition. The operation of subtracting 1 from 2 $(2 - 1)$ means that one unit is to be *taken away* from two units, leaving a remainder of one unit. In contrast to addition, the commutative and associative laws do *not* hold for subtraction. Therefore, as indicated in the following examples, we have

$8 - 4 = 4$	but	$4 - 8 = -4$
$3 - 6 = -3$	but	$6 - 3 = +3$
$8 - 3 - 2 = 3$	but	$3 - 2 - 8 = -7$
$9 - 4 - 2 = 3$	but	$2 - 4 - 9 = -11$

In subtracting negative numbers, we must remember that subtracting a negative number produces the same result as adding a positive number. Thus we have

$4 - (-3) = +7$	$4 + 3 = 7$
$8 - (-10) = +18$	$8 + 10 = 18$

D. *Multiplication*

The operation of multiplication actually is a short cut method of adding when the same number is to be added several times. For example, if 7 is to be added three times $(7 + 7 + 7)$, we can equivalently multiply 7 by 3 to obtain a product of 21.

In multiplication, as in addition, the commutative laws and associative laws are in operation so that

$a \times b = b \times a$

$4 \times 5 = 5 \times 4 = 20$

$(2 \times 5) \times 6 = 10 \times 6 = 60$

A third law of multiplication, the *distributive* law, applies to the multiplication of one number by the sum of several other numbers. Thus,

$$a\,(b + c) = ab + ac$$
$$2\,(3 + 4) = 2\,(7) = 2\,(3) + 2\,(4) = 14$$

Here the resulting product is the same regardless of whether b and c are summed and multiplied by a or a is multiplied by b and by c and the two products then added together. Furthermore, in multiplying negative numbers, we should remember that a negative number multiplied by a negative number equals a positive number. Thus,

$$(-a) \times (-b) = ab$$
$$(-5) \times (-4) = +20$$

E. *Division*

Just as subtraction is the opposite of addition, division is the opposite or inverse of multiplication. When we discussed multiplication, we viewed it as a shortcut to addition in certain situations. In a similar manner, division can be thought of in terms of subtraction. When we divide 20 by 4, we are actually determining the number of times that 4 can be subtracted from 20. However, in general, the number of times that one number can be divided by another does not have to be an exact integer value since there could be a remainder. For example, if 21 rather than 20 were divided by 4, we would have an answer of 5 with a remainder of 1, or $5\frac{1}{4}$.

As in the case of subtraction, neither the commutative nor associative laws of addition hold for division so that

$$a \div b \neq b \div a$$
$$9 \div 3 \neq 3 \div 9$$
$$6 \div (3 \div 2) = 4$$
$$(6 \div 3) \div 2 = 1$$

Moreover, the distributive law will only hold when the numbers to be added are contained in the numerator, not the denominator. Thus,

$$\frac{a + b}{c} = \frac{a}{c} + \frac{b}{c} \quad \text{but} \quad \frac{a}{b + c} \neq \frac{a}{b} + \frac{a}{c}$$

For example,

$$\frac{6 + 9}{3} = \frac{6}{3} + \frac{9}{3} = 2 + 3 = 5$$

but

$$\frac{1}{2 + 3} = \frac{1}{5} \neq \frac{1}{2} + \frac{1}{3}$$

The final, important property of division is that if the numerator and denominator are both multiplied or divided by the same number, the resulting quotient will not be affected. Therefore, if we have

$$\frac{80}{40} = 2$$

then

$$\frac{5\,(80)}{5\,(40)} = \frac{400}{200} = 2$$

and

$$\frac{80 \div 5}{40 \div 5} = \frac{16}{8} = 2$$

F. *Fractions*

A fraction is a number that consists of a combination of whole numbers and/or parts of whole numbers. For instance, the fraction $\frac{1}{6}$ consists only of a portion of a number, while the fraction $\frac{7}{6}$ consists of the whole number 1 plus the fraction $\frac{1}{6}$. Each of the operations of addition, subtraction, multiplication, and division can be applied to fractions. When adding or subtracting fractions, one must obtain the lowest common denominator for each fraction prior to adding or subtracting them. Thus, in adding $\frac{1}{3} + \frac{1}{5}$, the lowest common denominator is 15 so that we have $\frac{5}{15} + \frac{3}{15} = \frac{8}{15}$. In subtracting $\frac{1}{4} - \frac{1}{6}$, the same principle can be applied so that we would have a lowest common denominator of 12, producing a result of $\frac{3}{12} - \frac{2}{12} = \frac{1}{12}$.

The operations of multiplication and division of fractions are not complicated by the lowest common denominator requirement of addition and subtraction. Thus, if $\frac{a}{b}$ is multiplied by $\frac{c}{d}$ we obtain

$$\frac{a \times c}{b \times d}.$$

That is, the resulting numerator is the product of the numerators (a and c) while the denominator is the product of the two denominators (b and d). The resulting fraction can sometimes be reduced to a lower term by dividing numerator and denominator by a common factor. For example, taking $\frac{2}{3} \times \frac{6}{7} = \frac{12}{21}$ and dividing numerator and denominator by 3, produces a result of $\frac{4}{7}$.

Division of fractions can be thought of as the inverse of multiplication, so that the divisor could be inverted and multiplied by the original fraction; that is,

$$\frac{9}{5} \div \frac{1}{4} = \frac{9}{5} \times \frac{4}{1} = \frac{36}{5}$$

$$2 \div \frac{3}{7} = \frac{2}{1} \times \frac{7}{3} = \frac{14}{3}$$

Finally, the division of a fraction can be thought of as a way of converting the fraction to a decimal. For example, the fraction $\frac{2}{5}$ can be converted to a decimal by simply dividing its numerator (2) by its denominator (5) to produce the decimal 0.40.

G. *Exponents and Square Roots*

The procedure of exponentiation provides a shortcut in writing out numerous multiplications. For example, if we have 2 x 2 x 2 x 2 x 2, then we may also write this as 2^5 or 32. The 5 represents the exponent of the number 2, telling us that 2 is to be multiplied by itself 5 times.

There are several rules that can be applied for multiplying or dividing numbers that contain exponents.

Rule 1. If two numbers involving powers of the *same* number are multiplied, the product is that same number exponentiated to the sum of the powers ($x^a \cdot x^b = x^{a+b}$). Thus, $4^2 \cdot 4^3 = (4 \cdot 4)(4 \cdot 4 \cdot 4) = 4^5$

Rule 2. If we take the power of a number which is already taken to a power, the result will be the number exponentiated to the *product* of the two powers $\left((x^a)^b = x^{ab}\right)$. For example,

$$(2^2)^3 = (2^2)(2^2)(2^2) = 2^6$$

Rule 3. If one number raised to a power is divided by the same number raised to a power, the quotient will be that number exponentiated to the difference of the powers $\left(\dfrac{x^a}{x^b} = x^{a-b}\right)$. Thus,

$$\frac{3^5}{3^3} = \frac{\cancel{3} \cdot \cancel{3} \cdot \cancel{3} \cdot 3 \cdot 3}{\cancel{3} \cdot \cancel{3} \cdot \cancel{3} \cdot 1 \cdot 1} = 3^2$$

If the denominator has a higher power, the resulting quotient will be a negative power. Thus,

$$\frac{3^3}{3^5} = \frac{\cancel{3} \cdot \cancel{3} \cdot \cancel{3} \cdot 1 \cdot 1}{\cancel{3} \cdot \cancel{3} \cdot \cancel{3} \cdot 3 \cdot 3} = \frac{1 \cdot 1}{3 \cdot 3} = \frac{1}{3^2} = 3^{-2}$$

If the difference between the power of the numerator and denominator is 1, the result will be the actual number itself, so that $x^1 = x$. For example,

$$\frac{3^3}{3^2} = \frac{\cancel{3} \cdot \cancel{3} \cdot 3}{\cancel{3} \cdot \cancel{3} \cdot 1} = 3^1 = 3$$

If, however, there is no difference in the power of the number in the numerator and denominator, the result will be 1. Thus,

$$\frac{x^a}{x^a} = x^{a-a} = x^0 = 1$$

Therefore, any number exponentiated to the zero power will equal 1. For example,

$$\frac{3^3}{3^3} = \frac{\cancel{3} \cdot \cancel{3} \cdot \cancel{3}}{\cancel{3} \cdot \cancel{3} \cdot \cancel{3}} = 3^0 = 1$$

The square root represents a special power of a number, the $\frac{1}{2}$ power. It indicates the value that when multiplied by itself will produce the original number. It is given by the symbol $\sqrt{}$. Thus, $\sqrt{x}$ represents the number which, when squared, produces the number x. For example, the square root of 25 $\left(\sqrt{25}\right)$ is 5 since $5^2 = 25$.

Square roots can readily be obtained in two ways:

    (a) by direct square root calculation
    (b) by using an electronic calculator

The first way, direct calculation, usually involves tedious computations using long divisions. The second way, using an electronic calculator, requires us to choose a calculator that contains the square root function.

ANSWERS TO QUIZ

Part I	1. 3/2	2. .16	3. 5/3	4. 1/81	5. 0.20
	6. 1.30	7. −6.4	8. +1/6	9. 3/200	10. 4
Part II	1. c	2. c	3. a	4. b	5. a
	6. b	7. d	8. b	9. a	10. c

REFERENCE: W.L. Baslow, *Mathematics for Statistics;* New York: John Wiley & Sons, 1969.

ANSWERS TO
MULTIPLE CHOICE QUESTIONS

Chapter 1   1. c   2. a   3. d   4. e   5. f   6. b   7. a   8. f   9. a
                  10. f 11. b 12. e

Chapter 2   1. a   2. b   3. b   4. a   5. c   6. a   7. b   8. d   9. d
                  10. c 11. c 12. d 13. b 14. d 15. d

Chapter 3   1. b   2. d   3. d   4. a   5. a   6. d   7. a

Chapter 4   1. b   2. b   3. a   4. d   5. b   6. d   7. a

Chapter 6   1. a   2. d   3. b   4. a   5. b   6. a   7. a   8. b   9. b
                  10. a 11. c 12. a 13. d 14. c 15. a 16. d

Chapter 7   1. d   2. a   3. c   4. b   5. a   6. b   7. d

Chapter 8   1. d   2. d   3. c   4. b   5. d   6. c   7. c   8. d   9. d
                  10. d

Chapter 9   1. b   2. a   3. d   4. a   5. b   6. c   7. d   8. c   9. d
                  10. b

Chapter 10   1. b   2. c   3. d   4. c   5. a   6. b   7. b   8. c

Chapter 11   1. a   2. b   3. b   4. c   5. a   6. d   7. c   8. b   9. d

Chapter 12   1. d   2. a   3. b   4. a   5. c

Chapter 13   1. b   2. c   3. d   4. a   5. b   6. d   7. a

Chapter 14   1. b   2. c   3. a   4. b   5. d

Chapter 15   1. d   2. d   3. a   4. c   5. d   6. b

Chapter 16   1. d   2. d   3. b   4. a   5. c   6. c   7. d   8. b   9. a

Chapter 17   1. d   2. b   3. b   4. b   5. d   6. a   7. b   8. c   9. b

Chapter 18   1. c   2. a   3. d   4. b   5. a   6. b   7. c   8. d   9. d
                  10. d 11. d 12. d

Chapter 19   1. d   2. a   3. b   4. d   5. d   6. d   7. d   8. d   9. b